Foreword

Most food originates from farms but reaches the consumer through retail and catering outlets, passing on the way through various intermediaries - including marketing organisations, and food manufacturers and processors - trading and operating around the globe. Increasingly, however, companies at all points in the food production chain have to remain aware of what their customer and ultimately the consumer wants: the market is highly competitive, food safety and quality are scrutinised like never before, and there is an expectation of a consistent supply of high quality food.

Systems have evolved to enable this - including, for example, quality and safety assurance schemes, traceability, product specifications and independent auditing. These have developed hand-in-hand with much greater communication between primary producers and the businesses they supply along the production chain. In short, the 'food' and 'agriculture' sectors now work more closely than ever before and have a greater mutual understanding of the priorities and constraints they each face.

In recognition of this there is greater interaction between many of the organisations whose technical support underpins different sectors in the food chain. As leaders in their fields, CCFRA and RASE have been working together to serve better the needs of the agri-food chain. This short book is a tangible example of this collaboration, which, with the complementary volume on food manufacturing, will help food companies and agricultural enterprises better understand each other and work more closely together.

Colin Dennis - Campden & Chorleywood Food Research Association

Mike Calvert - Royal Agricultural Society of England

SERIES PREFACE

Food and food production have never had a higher profile, with food-related issues featuring in newspapers or on TV and radio almost every day. At the same time, educational opportunities related to food have never been greater. Food technology is taught in schools, as a subject in its own right, and there is a variety of food-related courses in colleges and universities - from food science and technology through nutrition and dietetics to catering and hospitality management.

Despite this attention, there is widespread misunderstanding of food - about what it is, about where it comes from, about how it is produced, and about its role in our lives. One reason for this, perhaps, is that the consumer has become distanced from the food production system as it has become much more sophisticated in response to the developing market for choice and convenience. Whilst other initiatives are addressing the issue of consumer awareness, feedback from the food industry itself and from the educational sector has highlighted the need for short focused overviews of specific aspects of food science and technology with an emphasis on industrial relevance.

The *Key Topics in Food Science and Technology* series of short books therefore sets out to describe some fundamentals of food and food production and, in addressing a specific topic, each issue emphasises the principles and illustrates their application through industrial examples. Although aimed primarily at food industry recruits and trainees, the series will also be of interest to those interested in a career in the food industry, food science and technology students, food technology teachers, trainee enforcement officers and, established personnel within industry seeking a broad overview of particular topics.

Leighton Jones
Series Editor

PREFACE TO THIS VOLUME

Material flows along the food production chain from the primary producer - that is the farmer or grower - to the consumer. Sometimes the transfer between these two is direct (e.g. through farm shops or farmers' markets). More commonly, it involves one or more intermediaries including marketing organisations (e.g. produce marketing organisations, abattoirs, grain merchants, brokers and wholesalers), processors, manufacturers, ingredients suppliers and retailers that make up the food supply chain.

Although historically the 'agriculture' and 'food' sectors have viewed themselves as separate, this situation is rapidly changing as the supply chain becomes much more closely integrated. For example, in the early 1990s, concepts such as quality management and safety assurance (e.g. HACCP) were relatively new to many food companies. But now that they are well established in this part of the chain they are increasingly being adopted by farmers and growers in response to both commercial (i.e. customer) and regulatory pressures. Companies at all points in the food production chain are increasingly working together to assure food safety and quality and to meet the needs of consumers in a dynamic marketplace

Despite the closer links between 'agricultural' and 'food' enterprises, however, there is still considerable scope for better mutual understanding of their respective activities, practices and perspective. This short book was written to help encourage this. It describes what agriculture is, outlines the basis of some practices, explains some terminology and highlights some of the constraints faced by food producers in the context of the food supply chain. It is intended as a brief introduction, not as an in-depth review, but it provides a lead-in to more detailed information sources already available.

Chris Knight, Richard Stanley and Leighton Jones
CCFRA

ACKNOWLEDGEMENTS

We are grateful to colleagues for their constructive comments and advice at various stages in the preparation of this book, including Martin Hall (CCFRA), Dr. Steven Walker (CCFRA), Angela Lea (RASE), Alan Spedding (RASE), Ellen Quinn (CCFRA), Sue Salmon (CCFRA), Richard Trow-Smith (Crop Protection Association), Caroline Drummond (LEAF) and David Haine (Sainthill Farm, Gloucester). Some of the examples used to illustrate specific points are based on other CCFRA publications and we are grateful to the authors of these, as cited, for providing the source material. Finally we thank Janette Stewart for the artwork and design.

NOTE

All legislation, codes of practice and guidelines mentioned in this publication are included for the purpose of illustration only.

The nature, scope, content and approach of legislation and self-regulation vary widely between countries and regions of the world. The examples used in this book relate primarily to UK and/or EU practice unless otherwise stated.

CONTENTS

1. INTRODUCTION

1.1 Agriculture in perspective

Most of the food we eat comes from crops and livestock that are farmed specifically for that purpose. With the exception of fish, game, and some wild nuts, berries and fruits, we eat very little from the wild. The development of farming systems, as mankind progressed from hunter-gatherer to a more settled existence, provided us with greater control over our food supply. Cultivation of crops and husbandry of livestock allowed better nurturing, more effective protection from pests and diseases, and, gradually, selection of 'strains' with the best characteristics to improve crops and livestock.

The mechanisation and intensification of farming might initially have been embraced during the agricultural revolution in the eighteenth century, but during the twentieth century the adoption of increasingly sophisticated agricultural and processing technologies secured a steady food supply on a scale that would otherwise have been impossible. The emergence of genetics as a science in its own right during the twentieth century played its part too as strategies for breeding crops and livestock with precisely the characteristics desired became possible. In the developed world, effective production, preservation, processing, storage and transportation systems have provided for a balanced diet of safe, wholesome and nutritious foods.

Agriculture sits between the work of plant and animal breeders on the one hand and manufacturers and distributors (including retailers) on the other. It is the job of farmers to use the best crops and livestock available and work within environmental constraints and available additional 'inputs' to provide a consistent supply of food. Some of this is then distributed and consumed with little, if any, further processing while much passes through an elaborate and sophisticated production chain.

In some cases, further processing is essential just to make the raw material edible - the conversion of flour to bread being a good example. In other cases, processing might simply be desirable as a way of 'smoothing out' the food supply - the production of jams and pickles provides an example of this. A natural extension of this is in the development of new products to exploit or create markets, helping companies to develop or retain a competitive edge (see Hutton, 2001)

An interesting feature of agricultural food production of the last ten or so years, and one which is still very much on-going, is its closer integration into the food supply chain. Increasingly farmers produce food and raw materials for specific purposes and with specific markets in mind - supplying fruits or vegetables to a produce marketing organisation or a major retailer, for example, or growing crops under contract for a particular processor or manufacturer. This has had all kinds of implications for farming practices and farm businesses. Increasingly farmers have to embrace concepts such as quality management, safety and quality assurance, and product traceability. At the same time, it has enabled the farmer's customer (e.g. manufacturer, retailer) to provide clear feedback on consumer trends which can then influence production practices. Examples of this include the moves towards integrated crop management and organic production systems (e.g. away from chemical inputs), and higher priorities attached to animal welfare issues.

The purpose of this book is to provide a broad impression of the modern food production chain as viewed from the agricultural part of the chain. Taken with the complementary volume on food manufacturing, it will help encourage better mutual understanding between the agricultural and food sectors. It does not provide a detailed discussion of the economics of agricultural systems nor a guide to specific agricultural practices as this is covered in detail elsewhere (e.g. Soffe, 1995). Nor does it consider in their own right the industries allied to farming such as plant and animal breeding, agrochemical production or animal feed production. Rather, it describes and illustrates some of the technical and commercial trends and pressures within the integrated food supply chain that are shaping the modern agricultural food production sector and the relationships between food producers (farmers and growers) and food manufacturers and retailers.

Box 1 - Integrated

The term integrated is used in two distinct ways, which can cause confusion. The first way in which the term is used is to refer to integrated farming methods such as integrated farm management, which includes integrated crop management (ICM) and integrated pest management (IPM) (see p40 and Glossary for further information on these).

The second way in which the word 'integrated' is used, is to refer to the 'integrated food chain' or 'integrated supply chain'. This is simply a shorthand way of referring to the closer trading and communications links between all parties within the industrial food supply chain - especially between food producers (farmers and growers in the 'agricultural sector') and food manufacturers, processors and retailers (companies that make up the 'food sector'). Also implicit within this use of the word 'integrated', is the adoption by the agricultural part of the chain of systems of safety assurance (e.g. HACCP), quality management and traceability, that are now well established in food manufacturing and retailing.

1.2 What is agriculture?

Agriculture is the system and processes used in the cultivation of plants and raising of animals for food and other materials. There are many types of agriculture which can be variously classified on the basis of what is being farmed (e.g. livestock, cereals, fruits and vegetables, non-food materials such as fibres and so on) and the way in which it is being farmed. Horticulture, for example, is the term usually used for the cultivation of vegetables, fruits, flowers, and ornamental shrubs and trees, while arable farming is taken to include the cultivation of cereals and oilseed crops.

Another way of looking at agriculture is the type of system employed and the philosophy underlying the approach. This approach is taken by Tinker (2000) in his introduction to agriculture in which he distinguishes between three farming systems: intensive (conventional) agriculture, organic farming and integrated farming. These approaches are considered in more detail in the next chapter, but whichever is employed, modern farmers will, for the large part, use livestock and crops that have been bred specifically for the purpose of food production and which also owe their current usage to their geographical redistribution by man (see Box 2 - p4).

Box 2 - Geographical origin of some major crops

Mankind has been heavily instrumental in changing the genetic make-up and geographical distribution of many of the world's crop plants. Some crops look very different from their wild ancestors and from existing related species, as a result of extensive selective breeding. In some instances the ancestry of existing crop species is far from clear. For example, bread wheat *Triticum aestivum* appears to have no immediate wild ancestor and is believed to have arisen from hybridsiation of closely related species. This accounts for its unusual genetic make-up (genotype) as it has three paired sets of chromosomes (hexaploid) not one paired set (diploid) as is the case for most organisms. Domestication has also created edible crops from poisonous plants - potato and tomato (glycoalkaoids), brassicas (gluconsinolates), oilseed rape (erucic acid), and various legumes (lectins, trypsin inhibitors) provide good examples.

Domestication of wild types has gone hand-in-hand with geographical redistribution. The potato and the tomato, for example, are native of the Americas but are now grown throughout the temperate regions. Soya and rice, native of Asia, are now grown on an enormous scale in the Americas. This table compares the geographical origins of some crops with their current regions of cultivation.

Species	Origin	Cultivated
Apple (*Malus* x domestica) and Pear (*Pyrus communis*)	Central Asia	Temperate regions world-wide
Banana (*Musa* spp.)	SE Asia/Western Pacific	Tropical, subtropical
Barley (*Hordeum vulgare*)	South Asia	Temperate world
Beans: runner (*Phaseolus coccineus*) and French (*Phaseolus vulgaris*)	Central America	Tropics, sub-tropics and temperate areas world-wide
Cocoa (*Theobroma cacao*)	Upper Amazon	Central & South America, Central Africa
Coffee (*Coffea arabica*)	Ethiopia	Latin America, India, Indonesia, East Africa
Grape (*Vitis vinifera*)	Middle East	Warm temperate areas
Groundnut (*Arachis hypogaea*)	Andes	Semi-arid tropics, subtropics and warm temperate regions
Maize (*Zea mays*)	Central America	Worldwide tropical and subtropical regions

Species	Origin	Cultivated
Oats (*Avena sativa*)	Northern Europe	Russia and Northern Europe
Oil palm (*Elaeis guineensis*)	West Africa	West Africa, South East Asia, Latin America
Oilseed rape (*Brassica napus*)	Europe	Canada, Europe, China, India
Olives (*Olea europea*)	Middle East	Europe, Africa, Americas, Australia
Pea (*Pisum sativum*)	South West Asia	Temperate and cool sub-tropical regions
Potato (*Solanum tuberosum*)	S. American Andes	Throughout temperate world
Rice (*Oryza sativa*)	South Asia	Asia, Africa, Middle East, Americas
Soybean (*Glycine max*)	Asia	Warm temperate, esp. Americas
Sugar beet (*Beta vulgaris*)	Europe and West Asia	Europe and North America
Sugarcane (*Saccharum officinarum*)	Indo-China	Tropical, subtropical worldwide
Sunflower (*Helianthus annuus*)	North America	North America, Argentina, Europe, Russia
Tea (*Camellia sinensis*)	South East Asia	Sub-tropical Asia
Tomato (*Lycopersicon esculentum*)	Tropical America	Temperate world
Wheat (*Triticum aestivum*)	Middle East	Temperate world

Further reading:

Anon. (1990) Exploited plants: collected papers from Biologist. Institute of Biology, London.

Duddington, C.L. (1969) Useful plants. McGraw Hill.

Heywood, U.H. and Chant, S.R. (1982) Popular encyclopedia of plants. Cambridge University Press.

Moore, D.M. (Ed) (1982) Green planet: the story of plant life on earth. pp238-248. Domestication of plants. Cambridge University Press.

Smartt, J. and Simmonds, N.W. (1995) Evolution of crop plants. Second edition. Longman Scientific and Technical.

Vaughan, J.G and Geissler, C.A. (1997) The new Oxford book of food plants. Oxford University Press.

1.3 Towards an integrated food supply chain

Material flows along the food production chain, from the primary producer (i.e. farmer and grower) to the consumer via manufacturers, processors, retailers and food service outlets (caterers). This chain, which is illustrated in Figure 1, has become increasingly complex, as it has embraced the proliferation in product choice for consumers, the development of markets for convenient and pre-prepared foods, the rapid movement of goods by modern transportation, faster communication facilitating global trade, and increasingly competitive markets. The food industry is now much more sensitive and responsive to the perceived requirements of the consumer, and as the food supply chain becomes more closely integrated this trend is as significant for the farmer as it is for the retailer.

A retailer will typically sell branded and own-label products side by side. A single formulated product assembled in the UK, for example, might contain ingredients sourced from mainland Europe, Asia and the Americas. A single ingredient such as soyabean lecithin might pass through several hands between the farmer and the food manufacturer. The farmer will harvest the beans which will be transported, warehoused, mixed with other beans, bought by brokers, sold on to suppliers and then processed and fractionated. These different fractions (e.g. oil, flakes) may in turn be sold separately before further fractionation by ingredients processors and suppliers. While some ingredients are sourced in this way from the 'open market' others may be produced under contract - where a farmer and/or processor is contracted to a manufacturer to produce major ingredients (e.g. potatoes for use in a snack product).

Either way - whether sourcing materials direct or on the open market - the farmer's customer will almost certainly exercise a degree of control over the material being sourced. This includes:

- Specifications defining the quality of raw materials and end-products, which form the basis of trading agreements
- Product and ingredient identification and traceability systems
- Standard procedures to ensure that products are grown in a consistent way to assure that they deliver end-products of the quality required
- HACCP systems to assure product safety

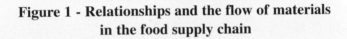

Figure 1 - Relationships and the flow of materials in the food supply chain

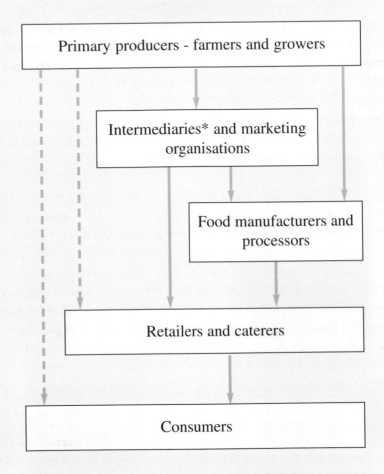

In the context of the food supply chain, companies often refer to companies which provide goods to them as 'suppliers' and to the companies that they supply with product or materials as 'customers'. The word 'consumer' is used to refer to the ultimate customer - i.e the person who buys and/or consumes the food. Within the chain, farmers and growers are the primary producers, while intermediaries* can include abattoirs, produce marketing organisations, grain merchants, brokers and wholesalers. This terminology - especially the terms supplier, customer and consumer - is used throughout this book as it helps make some important distinctions. Although some primary producers will supply direct to consumers, most food material produced on farms first passes through one or more other food businesses.

Box 3 - Agriculture under pressure

UK agriculture has witnessed some significant trends in the last two decades. Although exacerbated by the problems of BSE and Foot and Mouth, the trends seem to reflect a longer-term process of adjustment, and some have been mirrored on continental Europe. For example:

- Agricultural output as measured by volume has increased – that for 1999 was about 5% higher than the 1988/90 average. In contrast, the value of the output for these two periods was the same, at around £13bn.

- Agriculture's contribution to GDP has declined steadily - from around 2.2% in 1982 to 1.4% in 1990 and down to around 0.8% in 2001. This partly reflects the downward trend in farm prices (i.e. the value as opposed to the volume of agricultural output) but is also partly due to the growth of other sectors.

- Although consumer expenditure on food increased by around 40% over the period 1990-2000 (from £62bn to £88bn), the value of total sales of food raw materials produced by the agriculture sector remained steady at around £20bn. In other words, most of the growth in consumer expenditure relates to value added further along the chain.

- Hired labour employed in agriculture fell by about 40% between 1982 and 2000, with a relative increase in the proportion of part-time and casual workers.

- Environmental issues are increasingly the focus of attention, with a greater expectation on the role of farmers as custodians of the countryside.

- Food safety and quality has been the subject of unprecedented levels of scrutiny, leading to the development of systems for safety and quality assurance and traceability, and a general scepticism of the involvement of science and technology in food production.

Whilst these are only examples, and are not all specific to agriculture, together they have been highly significant for farm businesses and have shaped the way agriculture sits in the food production chain.

Further reading:

Curry, D. (2002) Farming and food: a sustainable future. Report of the Policy Commission on the Future of Farming and Food. See www.cabinet-office.gov.uk/farming

Marsh, J. (2001) Agriculture in the UK – its role and challenge. Foresight Report. Department of Trade and Industry. www.foresight.gov.uk

Clearly there is greater scope for this where there is a direct trading relationship between the farmer and manufacturer or retailer, but as the example with GM soya shows (see Box 36, p95) the situation can change rapidly for any particular ingredient. In general, however, the procedures reflect the move towards preventative approaches and have become an integral part of the way in which the many partners involved in the food production chain work together to develop and supply products that meet the needs and expectations of the consumer. As farming operations become more closely drawn into the chain, the expectation is that they will develop similar levels and compatible systems of 'total quality management'.

1.4 Agriculture and global trade

Agriculture is a global activity - it takes place in many parts of the world and many of its products are traded across and between nations and continents. The current international philosophy is that free trade, that is the unrestricted international trading of goods (including the products of agriculture), is in everyone's interests. Theoretically at least, it gives producers (suppliers) access to markets (demand) and vice versa. This clearly has significant political, economic and social implications, coverage of which is beyond the scope of this book. However, the way in which some of these impinge on industrial food production is worth considering - particularly GATT, the World Trade Organisation Agreement on Agriculture, international standards for food 'safety and quality' and, for the EU, the Common Agricultural Policy (CAP) - because they are often the source of much confusion.

1.4.1. GATT and the World Trade Organisation

GATT is the General Agreement on Tariffs and Trade. It was developed after World War Two to encourage freer trade and has been in operation since 1948. Its terms are periodically re-negotiated in 'Rounds', the last of which was the Uruguay Round, which started in 1986 and concluded in 1994. On conclusion of the Uruguay Round the World Trade Organisation (WTO) was created (on 1st January 1995) to carry negotiations forward. By mid-2001 over 140 countries had joined the WTO and around 30 others had membership applications pending.

Box 4 - Free trade and market distortion

A country that wants to protect part of its economy can subsidise production of products, subsidise export of these products, and discourage imports of the product (e.g. through import tariffs and non-tariff measures such as quotas). This can distort trade - i.e. create product volumes and prices that would not happen in a truly competitive market.

Governments might subsidise agricultural production for various reasons. Those most often presented include guaranteeing an adequate supply of food, protecting farmers from crop failures and fluctuations in world prices, and preserving rural economies. The downside to this is that subsidised production can lead to export subsidy wars in which countries with less to spend on subsidies suffer most. The Agreement on Agriculture (see Box 5) is an attempt to create balanced free trade and help prevent the problems that can arise from market distortion.

Further reading:

WTO (2001) Trading into the future. World Trade Organization webiste: www.wto.org/

Although historically some GATT rules applied to agriculture, others did not. The Uruguay Round changed this and resulted in a specific Agreement on Agriculture (AoA) which is now often referred to as WTO AoA. The aim of this is to increase free international trade of agricultural products and reduce 'market distortion' (see Box 4). It sets out commitments with which countries had to comply over the 'implementation period' (1995-2000), remains in force until a successor agreement has been renegotiated, and commits WTO members to further negotiations. In pursuance of freer trade, the Agreement on Agriculture commits the signatories to:

◆ Reducing domestic support (subsidies) for agricultural production
◆ Reducing import tariffs, maintaining existing import opportunities and creating new import opportunities
◆ Reducing the volume of and expenditure on export subsidies

This therefore has had significant implications for the EU's Common Agriculture Policy (see Box 5).

Box 5 - CAP: the common agricultural policy

The area that is now the European Union has seen many changes in its agricultural activities over the last forty or so years - agricultural changes which have proved significant not just for the production of food and other agricultural products, but also socially, economically and environmentally.

Precise long-term comparisons across the EU are difficult because of the periodic accession of new member states. However, a few figures illustrate some broad changes. In 1960, with a community of six, around 15 million people were employed in agriculture on 6.4 million farms. By the late 1980s this had fallen to around five and half million people on 4.8 million farms. During this time the average farm size increased from 12 ha to 20 ha. In short, agriculture declined as a source of employment in contrast to manufacturing and service industries, whilst farms became larger and more specialised. Historically there have also been significant differences between member states. In the late 1980s, for example, around 8% of the working population of the Community of Twelve was employed in agriculture, though this varied between states from less than 5% (e.g. UK and Netherlands) to around 30% (Greece).

The Common Agricultural Policy (CAP) was defined in the Treaty of Rome (1957), on the establishment of the European Economic Community (EEC) and has since been reformed several times. The initial aims of CAP, in the wake of post-War food shortages, the on-going cold-war, and the changes mentioned above, were to:

- secure an adequate and independent food supply
- stabilise prices for farmers and consumers
- help farmers to manage and safeguard the quality of the environment
- encourage social 'adjustment' in response to changing levels of agricultural employment
- manage the effects that changes in agriculture might have on closely related sectors (e.g. agricultural supply sectors)

These objectives have generally been pursued through 'market organisation'. In the case of some commodities, securing an adequate supply has been so successful that it became necessary to manage surpluses. This was achieved, at least in part, by restricting production capacity (e.g. applying quotas to milk production).

continued....

However, the main approaches to market organisation include:

- systems of subsidies for production and export of specific commodities
- controlling imports through tariffs and non-tariff measures
- direct market intervention - where specific agencies were established to buy products (e.g. cereals, butter, milk powder, sugar) in times of surplus for re-sale once the market had stabilised.

Because the production systems and markets for different commodities vary considerably, the approach adopted for each (e.g. production subsidies, export subsidies, import tariffs, intervention) also varies.

The on-going liberalisation of trade, through GATT and the WTO Agreement on Agriculture (see section 1.4 and the Glossary), coupled to changes in world markets and the challenges of the EU's eastward enlargement, has led to further CAP reforms, as part of the so-called Agenda 2000 reform package which itself is due for mid-term review in late 2002. The reforms include, for example, reducing market support prices for specific commodities, using direct aid rather than production subsidies as a means of supporting farm incomes, preparing for the accession of new member states, taking account of consumer concerns over food quality and safety, and integrating environmental goals into CAP.

Further reading:

European Union (1989) A common agricultural policy of the 1990s (5th Edition). Office for Official Publications of the European Communities.

Zervoudaki, S. (2000) The CAP reform - a policy for the future. Factsheet of European Commission - Directorate General of Agriculture.

The agreement does allow for special treatment (i.e. reduced commitments) for developing countries. It also includes a 'peace clause' which encourages signatories not to unreasonably challenge support measures used by other signatories; it is believed that this has reduced the number of disputes that might otherwise have arisen. A further feature of the agreement is that it provides ground rules (under the Sanitary and Phytosanitary Agreement) on trade restrictions adopted to protect human, animal and plant health. Although this allows countries to set their own rules it requires that their regulations are based on scientific rather than arbitrary judgements, and it encourages countries to use international standards, guidelines and recommendations where these exist.

1.4.2 Codex Alimentarius

Codex Alimentarius (the 'food code') provides internationally recognised standards, guidelines and recommendations relating to food safety and quality, and in so doing helps considerably in facilitating international trade. The responsibility for compiling the standards, guidelines and recommendations that make up the Codex Alimentarius rests with the Codex Alimentarius Commission. This is an international body which was created as a consequence of resolutions at conferences of the Food and Agriculture Organisation (FAO) in 1961 and World Health Organisation (WHO) in 1963. Membership of the Commission is open to all countries who are members of FAO and WHO and currently includes over 160 countries making up 97% of the world's population.

Much of the work of Codex is carried out by international working groups of experts drawn from governments, industry and the scientific community. The committees consult widely in formulating or revising standards that can then be justified on scientific grounds and which will help facilitate international trade and protect consumers. For example, the Sanitary and Phytosanitary Agreement mentioned previously makes specific reference to those parts of Codex Alimentarius dealing with issues such as veterinary drug and pesticide residues, contaminants, methods of sampling and analysis, and hygienic practice. These in turn provide a benchmark against which national standards and regulations can be evaluated to ensure that they are set at levels necessary to protect the health of a nation's consumers, animals and plants, but are not used as 'disguised' barriers to trade.

1.5 Agricultural food production

Modern agricultural systems have evolved over a long period of time and are still the subject of change. Intensification of farming and modern transportation methods mean that food is produced and internationally traded on an unprecedented scale. At the same time there is increasing awareness of and sensitivity to food safety and quality amongst consumers. The following chapters therefore look at agricultural food production from various angles - production and handling, food safety, food quality attributes, assurance of food safety and quality, and regulatory control.

Commercial crop and animal production operates on the fundamental principles of productivity from natural resources in a particular economic, political and social context. This context changes with time. Thus, artificial and manufactured inputs and energy can be added to the available natural resources in order to increase productivity and optimise quality, but only if profitability can be achieved and if compliance with the appropriate legal and other requirements can be maintained. It is within this context that the production of primary food products takes place, that is within the practicalities and economics of primary production and requirements of the rest of the food chain and within the legislative framework including food safety aspects.

This book will consider primary production in the context of the food supply chain with special reference to the UK and European Union at the present time, by presenting the principles which are generally applicable with specific examples. It is beyond the scope of the book to consider the practical aspects of primary production in detail for the many different products of the soil and stock rearing. It should be recognised however that husbandry practices change with the introduction of new inputs, including varieties and pest and disease control agents, improved understanding of biological and husbandry principles, and the development of new and efficient techniques and machinery. Primary production is also influenced by consumer and social requirements regarding the quality of food and the way it is produced, including care for the environment and animal welfare, as well as economic and political trends which change the relative value of inputs and outputs. It is within this context that the book considers agriculture or primary production as part of the modern food supply chain.

Box 6 - Crop production: the scale is enormous

The scale on which the world produces food crops is difficult to comprehend. According to official figures (FAO), the crop that the world produced most of in 2000 is sugar cane, and the amount produced was more than the amount of rice (ranked second) and maize (ranked third) combined. Not surprisingly, the countries with the largest areas and/or populations tend to produce the most food. China, for example, is the world's largest producer of rice, wheat, potatoes, apples and cabbages while the USA tops the league for maize and soya, Brazil for sugar cane and citrus fruits, the Russian Federation for barley and India for bananas and plantains.

The production of some crops is concentrated in relatively few countries. For example, in 2000, nearly 90% of the world's soya was produced by just four countries - the USA (47%), Brazil (20%), Argentina (12%) and China (10%) - the remaining 11% or so being produced by 78 different countries. The major contribution of the US to world soya was one of the factors that led to difficulties over GM soya in the UK (see Box 36 - p95). The top 5 major maize producing countries accounted for 72% of world output; for sugar cane the figure is 64%, and for wheat it is 53%. Not surprisingly, the world's largest producers of grapes are also major wine producers - Italy, France, USA and Spain together account for nearly 50% of the world's supply of grapes.

Table - The world's top twenty crops (by amount) in 2000 according to FAO figures*

Crop	Production
Sugar cane	1260
Rice	594
Maize	593
Wheat	584
Potatoes	321
Sugar beet	246
Cassava	174
Soyabeans	161
Sweet potatoes	142
Barley	132
Tomatoes	98
Bananas and plantains	96
Oranges	67
Grapes	64
Watermelons	63
Apples	59
Sorghum	57
Cabbages	54
Coconuts	51
Onions	50

*The amounts shown are in millions of metric tonnes.

Further reading:

A vast amount of statistical information on world production of crops and livestock can be accessed on the FAOSTAT Database on the website of the Food and Agriculture Organisation www.fao.org

Box 7 - Lands of milk and honey ... and meat and eggs

During year 2000, the world produced just over one and quarter million metric tonnes of honey according to the Food and Agriculture Organisation (FAO) - a lot of work by a lot of bees. At just over 1/4 million tonnes, China alone accounted for about one fifth of the total output. Other significant producers included Argentina (98,000 tonnes), USA (94,000), Mexico (59,000), Ukraine (52,000), India (51,000), Russia (50,000), and Canada and Spain (both 32,000). The UK produced just over 4,000 tonnes of honey.

The world also produced around 489 million tonnes of cow's milk during 2000. That equates to about 857 billion pints. In this case the FAO records the world's biggest producer as the USA (76 million tonnes), followed by India (34), Russian Federation (32), Germany (28), France (25), Brazil (22) and then the UK (15).

Table - World production of meat, eggs and milk during 2000 according to FAO figures*

Commodity	Production*
Pig meat	90
Beef	59
Chicken meat	58
Milk	486
Eggs	55

*The figures shown are in millions of metric tonnes.

Meanwhile the world's hens laid around 55 million metric tonnes of eggs - which equates to about 787 billion eggs. China alone accounted for about 42% of this, with the US (9%) a distant second. At 90 million metric tonnes, the amount of pig meat produced easily exceeded that of beef and chicken, and whilst China was the biggest producer of pigmeat (46% of world production), the USA was the leading producer of chicken (24% of world production) and beef (21%).

Reference:

A vast amount of statistical information on world production of crops and livestock can be accessed on the FAOSTAT Database on the website of the Food and Agriculture Organisation www.fao.org

2. PRODUCTION AND HANDLING PRACTICES

This chapter covers four broad aspects of primary production and handling of food materials on an agricultural scale: farming systems, production practices, hygienic handling practices, and environmental issues. Primary production is regarded as the range of horticultural and agricultural activities used in the production of both crops and livestock. The practicalities of crop and livestock production are necessarily fundamentally different, and so these enterprises are treated separately in this chapter. However, some general points about the types of farming systems in common use can be considered first, as the issues covered are common to both livestock and crop enterprises.

2.1 Farming systems

The business of food agriculture is one of running an enterprise which produces a marketable food commodity by controlled management of a biological system. Farming operations vary widely both in terms of the products they generate and the way in which these products are produced. Some examples of the major types of farming and growing operations are listed in Table 1.

Table 1 - The major categories of food farming

Type	Typical products
Arable	Cereals, oilseed, sugar beet
Horticulture and protected crops	Fruits, vegetables, salad crops
Cattle farming	Dairy and meat
Pig farming	Meat
Poultry farming	Meat and eggs
Sheep farming	Meat
Fish farming	Fish meat

Fruits, vegetables and grains are produced by providing a suitable environment for the crop to reach a suitable stage for harvest. This can only be done by management of the necessary inputs of seed, soil, water and nutrients, in addition to protecting the crop from damage by invasion of weeds, pests and diseases. Similarly, livestock operations involve providing a suitable environment for good livestock husbandry right the way through to 'harvesting' of the product. In both cases the success of the business relies on the correct balance of inputs (e.g. labour, materials) and the outputs, namely marketable products and waste.

The production of many primary products, including crops and animals, is increasingly a highly specialised operation. What was once a predominantly manual small-scale operation has become an intensive and in some cases highly mechanised agribusiness in which areas of production are well defined and developed. Fruits and vegetables for processing are a particular case in point. Some fresh produce may still be produced on small acreages, such as market garden enterprises, but most vegetables for processing are produced in large-scale and specialised operations more akin to agriculture than traditional horticulture. Such specialised production for the processing market has also gone hand-in-hand with the growth of a large and sophisticated food processing industry. As processing technologies have developed and the demand for processed products has increased, the demand for high quality raw materials suitable for a particular intended use has become more important.

Another changing feature of agriculture, at least in the UK and partly as a consequence of the developing sophistication of farming systems, is the increasing involvement of farm management companies and specialist agronomists. As with other industries many aspects of crop and livestock production require considerable technical knowledge and skills which are continuously being refined and improved through research and development activities. Many farmers therefore seek advice from other sources and only larger organisations such as farm management companies or specialist advisers have the necessary resources to keep their knowledge up to date. For example, decision making for the application of fertilisers and pesticides to crops is an increasingly complex matter and the use of these inputs has to be judged against the benefits of their use. Many different factors have to be considered, including the justification for use, choice of the most appropriate product and application rate and timing, in order to optimise outputs, in terms of yield and quality, while at the same time minimising the environmental impact.

The types and extent of input are a defining feature of the farming system used, as described by Tinker (2000) in his introduction to agriculture which distinguishes between three farming systems:

- **Intensive (conventional) agriculture** - although this covers a wide range of practices, it is characterised by the drive towards productivity and efficiency and implies using science and technology to its fullest extent

- **Organic farming** - although difficult to define precisely, this is generally regarded as a system which largely avoids the use of synthetic fertilisers, pesticides, growth regulators and feed additives and relies instead on crop rotation, natural fertilizers (e.g. green manures), and biological pest control.

- **Integrated farming** - often regarded as a half-way house between the above contrasting alternatives; integrated systems attempt to combine the best traditional approaches with appropriate modern technology to balance the need for economic production with positive environmental management.

In some respects, integrated farming is becoming less of a half-way house as increasingly the practices of integrated farming are assumed by so-called conventional agriculture. For example, there is an increasing trend away from a high input and routine application of agrochemicals (the traditional perception of conventional agriculture) to a more considered approach where fertilisers and pesticides are applied to meet the crop needs more precisely. This is in part a response to economic forces and market influences as well as concerns by farmers for the way in which they farm. Conventional agriculture is not a rigid system, it has changed in recent years and is likely to continue to do so. How long will it be therefore before integrated farming is the new conventional agriculture?

The three systems listed above reflect different philosophies and approaches which are covered in more detail later. In reality each farming business will be managed independently and not all will necessarily fit into one of the above categories. Current trends, particularly in Europe, are for farming systems to adopt more environmentally friendly management practices. There are now many integrated farming schemes in operation, which encourage biodiversity on the farm and minimise the use of inputs such as pesticides, fertilisers and veterinary medicines.

Box 8 - Organic diversity

The development of organic standards has occurred at different times in many countries. For example Germany and Austria have a long established organic growing philosophy arising from the Biodynamic movement in the 1930s and in the UK the Soil Association was founded in 1946. As a result there have been a small number of organic farms in Europe for many years. However, when the organic movement developed in the 1980s, more comprehensive standards were set and subsequently the EC Regulation 2092/91 (which came into force in 1991) provided for greater harmonisation of organic practices across the EU.

In other producer countries, the development of organic agriculture has been less well defined. In the USA for example, the certification of organic producers could only be carried out by the small number of States which had organic standards. A national organic standard for the USA has only recently been agreed, to take effect from 2002. The European and US authorities are currently agreeing terms of equivalence of the two standards so that each can be accepted when organic products are traded between the EU and USA. In most other producer countries the European standard is in use until individual countries can accredit their own national standard. The International Federation of Organic Agricultural Movements (IFOAM) has a responsibility for setting internationally compatible standards which will facilitate world trade in key organic commodities.

2.2 Crop production and handling

2.2.1 Background

For the farmer or grower the choice of crop is related to the potential yield and value of the output at harvest. Profitability of an enterprise is also dictated by the level of inputs required to bring the crop to a successful harvest.

Crops are grown in different climatic regions and soil types, so each crop will have minimum and optimum requirements that can be met by ensuring that suitable locations are used for crop production. For example, fruit crops which may be sensitive to frost will require sheltered, frost free conditions to give reliable yields. Potatoes can only be grown successfully on higher grade soils which are medium textured and relatively free of stones. Cereals will grow on lighter shallower soils and can tolerate fluctuations in temperature and rainfall, so are found in a wide range of climatic areas. Some fruits and vegetables are produced in a protected or semi-protected environment (e.g. glasshouses, polythene tunnels) which gives the grower far greater control over the environment. Some, for example, tomatoes, can be grown hydroponically - that is, with their roots in a solution of carefully controlled nutrient composition rather than in soil. Figure 2 depicts the main stages and inputs in potato production.

Crop production has become increasingly specialised with a tendency for each crop to be grown following a protocol or blueprint. The pattern of inputs used during a growing season will be influenced not just by circumstances (e.g. weather, pests, disease) but by the end use specification of the crop. Many crops have general requirements for drilling of seed, application of fertiliser, control of pests and diseases, and method of harvest. Within that framework, further detail may be provided, for example:

◆   specific varieties would be recommended for particular end uses

◆   rate of seed used or spacing of transplants will be specified to provide optimum crop development and plant size. Harvested product must adhere to specifications concerning size in order to meet pre-packing requirements.

◆   where irrigation is available it will be tailored to the needs of the crop and any additional requirement to maintain the crop roots at a prescribed level of soil moisture deficit, which will minimise fluctuations from stress due to natural rainfall cycles

◆   timing and rate of fertiliser use will be tailored to crop growth stage

◆   pesticide use may be limited to specified products

◆   storage conditions and transport time for harvested crops may be prescribed

Figure 2 - Main production stages of the potato crop depicted as a flow diagram

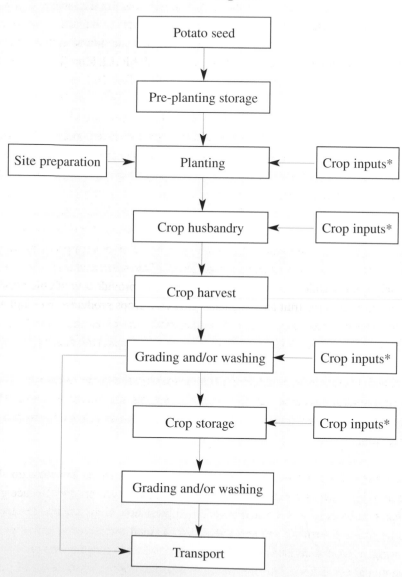

* Examples include pesticides, fertiliser, irrigation water, sprout suppressants.

The control of pests, diseases and weeds in crop production is usually achieved by a combination of cultural methods (including biological control - see Box 9) and pesticide applications. Decisions concerning the timing and rate of pesticide use are guided by the results of crop monitoring, which will identify the nature of pest, disease or weed present; this is related to threshold levels of infestation at which control is necessary. This approach is being developed and demonstrated by many farmers and farming related organisations such as LEAF (Linking Environment and Farming) in the UK and is covered in further detail in Box 16 (see p40). The concept of integrated farming is also being extended to the whole farm including mixed farming operations, that is those involving both animal and crop production. The principles and practices of integrated farming are therefore not just focussed on crop production but can embrace a more holistic, whole farm approach. In short, integrated farming practices are becoming more widely accepted by both the farming and food industries.

For fruit and vegetable production, the general requirements for crop production are described in a set of crop protocols, which must be adhered to by growers who are members of the Assured Produce Scheme (APS). This scheme was set up by the National Farmers Union and the UK food retailers to provide a verifiable standard of crop production for fruit and vegetable growers. Crops produced in compliance with the APS protocols are eligible to be marketed with the British Farm Standard Red Tractor Logo (see Chapter 5 and Box 32 on p87 for further details).

Cereal and oilseed growers can join a similar scheme called the Assured Combinable Crops Scheme (ACCS) - this also sets out crop management and food safety objectives which must be adhered to if producers are to meet registration requirements.

Most farmers and growers aim to minimise pesticide use when following good agricultural practice but some choose to follow organic systems which place greater emphasis on biodiversity and sustainability of the whole farm. Organic production includes limiting fertiliser and pesticide use to a small number of specified products and using cultural techniques to replace the higher level of inputs seen in conventional agriculture. The production of organic crops is characterised by a significant level of controlling legislation in addition to production standards set by

Box 9 - Biological control in crop protection

Biological control is the control of agricultural pests and diseases through the use of organisms (including insects, fungi, bacteria and viruses) that prey upon the pest or pathogen. The controlling agent might be a predator, parasite or disease, and usually specifically targets the pest in question. There are many commercial suppliers of biological control agents. Biological control needs careful management so that it is complemented rather than adversely affected by chemical treatments or cultivation practices.

Greenhouses provide an excellent setting for biological control, as the environment is contained and conditions can be controlled. In the production of tomatoes, cucumbers and peppers, for example, whitefly (*Trialeurodes* sp.) and aphids (*Myzus* spp.) can be a problem - whitefly can damage a plant's growing points and their larvae can leave honeydew deposits on leaves and fruits, encouraging mould growth, while, in addition to physical damage, aphids also transmit plant viral diseases. Whitefly can be controlled by introducing the greenhouse whitefly parasitoid (*Encarsia formosa*) and aphids with aphid parasitoids (*Aphidius* spp). In both cases the parasitoids lay eggs in the insect pests, which then kill the pest as they mature. An alternative control for aphids is to introduce the predator midge *Aphidoletes*, which feeds on aphids. Biological controls like these are widely used in commercial production of cucumbers and tomatoes in the UK.

Biological control is not restricted to contained environments. The bacterium *Bacillus thuringiensis* (Bt) is well established in biological control of caterpillar pests of vegetables, orchards and maize, for example. It produces a crystalline protein which, when eaten by the larvae, kills them by destroying their gut lining. Perhaps the most extreme example, however, is in the use of biological control against plagues of locust. In Australia, CSIRO developed GreenGuard™ based on the fungus *Metarhizium* sp. Billed as a major alternative to chemical control, the fungus infects locusts through the body wall and kills the insect by physical obstruction of essential passages within the body. It is used as part of a preventative approach by spraying on to hoppers (young locusts), preventing them from breeding and thereby limiting the size of outbreaks.

Further information:

Copping, L.G. (1998) The BioPesticide Manual. British Crop Protection Council.

Biological control virtual information centre from http://ipmwww.ncsu.edu/

GreenGuard™ goes global - CSIRO Website 30 October 2001. www.csiro.au

an 'organic organisation' approved by UKROFS. Under European Regulation 2092/91, if a food product is marketed as organically grown, the production system must have been verified to comply with the requirements specified in the Regulation. This means that organic food products must have been inspected during production and the producer issued with a certificate of compliance with the Regulation. As a result, organic foods retain a clear identity and the consumer is assured that organic foods marketed within the European Union are subject to a structured control and inspection system. Although organic standards vary to some extent within the EU, largely for historical reasons, this variation is also significant internationally (see Box 8, p 20).

2.2.2 Crop variety

Within the range of options available to all growers, one of the most important decisions is the selection of variety to be grown. The plant breeding industry has developed a wide range of varieties within each crop type. Each will have different characteristics, for example, of yield, disease resistance, or cold tolerance. Varieties may be early or late maturing within a season and may be ready for harvest during a short period or have an extended period of maturity. Size and colour will be variety-specific as will many other aspects of the appearance of fruits and vegetables; these are becoming increasingly important in an environment where there is an increasing consumer desire for greater choice within each crop commodity. Each characteristic will make a variety suitable for specific uses and will enable varieties to fit into cropping programmes which require continuity of production for as long a season as possible.

2.2.3 Growing season and continuity of supply

A vital element of crop marketing is the ability to supply the commodity for as long a season as possible. Most retailers ask their suppliers to pack fruit and vegetables every week of the year. For some crops like onions, apples, potatoes and cabbage this may not present a problem; these crops are grown over a long season and can be stored for relatively lengthy periods using facilities which provide optimum conditions to maintain supplies throughout the year (see Box 10 - p28). However,

Table 2 - Examples of variety diversity for selected crops

Cauliflower	Season of maturity early-late
	Resistance to colour defects in adverse weather
	White types and green types
	Mini cauliflower
Potatoes	Early season new potatoes
	Maincrop large potatoes
	High dry matter suitable for chips/crisps
	Naturally dormant types are more suitable for long term storage
	Low dry matter varieties for canning and salad use
	Potato blight resistance for ICM and organic systems
Vining peas	Earliness/lateness to spread harvest season
	Large/small size to meet market requirements
	Uniform maturity to permit machine harvest
Lettuce	Crisp lettuce (iceberg type)
	Little Gem type
	Large leafed cos types
	Endive/Radicchio
	Resistance to bolting
	Resistance to common fungal diseases
Wheat	Hard wheats suitable for breadmaking
	Durum wheats suitable for pasta
	Soft wheats used for biscuit manufacture

where crops cannot be stored for any significant period of time suppliers must consider the co-ordination of their production over a range of climatic regions. In the UK, many crops can be planted and harvested earlier in the season in the south than in the north; there is a general trend for later supplies of many fruits and vegetables from the north of England and Scotland.

However, for continuity of supply of many crops over a 12 month period it is necessary to co-ordinate production with growers in southern European countries or from the African continent. A common scenario for supply of lettuce to UK supermarkets is to use UK growers from June to October when the crop is in season in Britain, then during the winter months supplies would be sourced from growers in Spain where the climate for the crop is favourable in the milder Mediterranean conditions (see Box 11 - p30). The role of the UK supplier is to provide technical support which will co-ordinate the crop production systems of UK and Spanish growers so that there is a continuous supply of lettuce of suitable quality every week of the year. This operation is repeated for a wide range of fresh fruit and vegetable crops with growers in Italy, Greece, Egypt, or Zimbabwe, for example, providing the UK winter supplies.

2.2.4 Crop handling

A key element in the handling and harvest of crops is the labour input required and its cost to the grower. The production and harvest of many crops has become increasingly mechanised in recent years in response to the advances in technology which have made automation possible and to the increasing difficulty in the recruitment of labour to perform agricultural tasks. Most field operations, such as cultivation, seed drilling, application of fertiliser and pesticides and harvesting, have been completely mechanised for many years in such crops as cereals, potatoes, carrots and peas and beans. However many field vegetable and fruit crops such as brassicas, salads and soft fruits as well as protected crops have traditionally been planted and harvested by hand with little mechanisation. With the increasing problem of obtaining an adequate labour force to grow these crops economically, a wide range of machines has been developed to do the job.

Box 10 - Production and storage cycles of selected crops

For each crop, the 'timelines' depict a single production and/or storage cycle over 2 calendar years, using the UK for illustrative purposes. For clarity, the repeat production cycle for the second year is ignored. The idea is to illustrate the time from planting to harvest and the extent to which the product can be stored; these features affect the availability of the product and influence the way in which manufacturers and retailers will source the materials from the UK and through importation.

For some products, such as lettuce and strawberry, the production cycles are relatively straightforward. A home-grown supply of crisp lettuce can be secured through sequential planting of different varieties (some of which mature quicker than others) in different regions of the country. Flat leaf lettuce, which can be grown in glass houses, is produced all year round in some parts of the UK. For strawberries, which are perennial crops and therefore in the ground between and through successive seasons, the UK supply can be extended by planting early and main-crop varieties and will also be affected by regional differences and the weather.

By comparison, the production cycle for cauliflowers, for example, is quite complex and requires careful planning to try to secure an almost year round supply of home grown product, as these again cannot be stored for any significant period. Some varieties can be planted late spring, grown through the summer and harvested early autumn. Others can be planted and grown through the summer and autumn, before harvest in the winter, while those varieties that are particularly cold tolerant can be grown right through the winter and harvested the following spring. The challenge to the grower is to extend the harvests for as long as possible to bridge the gaps that otherwise arise. This also depends on selecting the right varieties and to a large extent will also be influenced by the weather.

Early, second-early and main crop varieties of potato yield very different products, so although main crop potatoes can be stored for lengthy periods, this will not offset the need for imports of new potatoes, for example. Second earlies cannot be stored as long as main crop as they are more prone to sprouting. Although main-crop varieties can be stored for perhaps 9 months, they are unlikely to be used for the fresh produce market after this time, though will be perfectly adequate for processed products.

The UK produces predominantly winter wheat which is planted in the autumn and grown through the winter for harvest the following September. In contrast, spring wheat is planted around March but also harvested in September. Grain is highly durable and, if properly handled, can be stored for significant periods (several years) without loss of quality.

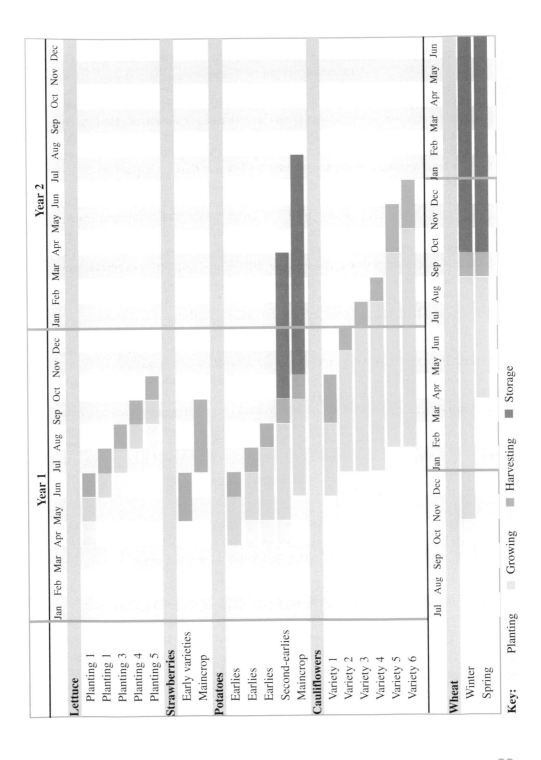

Box 11 - Sourcing a continuous supply of material for UK manufacturing or retailing

Again using the UK as an example, the way in which a manufacturer or retailer sources material to ensure a continuous supply will vary from crop to crop and will largely depend on the crop's production cycle. Lettuce for example, which cannot be stored for significant periods, can be sourced from UK growers while it is in season (from around May through to October) but has to be imported for the rest of the year. The same is true for other highly perishable crops such as strawberries and new potatoes. However, for crops which can be stored for longer periods - such as apples and carrots - the proportion of the year through which UK-produced material can be sourced is greater. However, importation of these is still important in order to fill the gaps that cannot be covered by storage, to offer the consumer a range of varieties and/or meet demand for volume.

Crop	Jan	Feb	Mar	Apr	May	Jun	Jul	Aug	Sep	Oct	Nov	Dec
Lettuce	Spain				UK						Spain	
Strawberries	Italy/Egypt	Spain			UK						Spain	
New potatoes	Egypt	Spain			UK						Spain	
Apples	UK	RSA	New Zealand				UK					
Carrots	UK		France/Spain		UK							

Examples of such developments can be illustrated by the use of mobile harvest rigs in lettuce fields to minimise handwork and transport of the crop and the successful introduction of machine harvesters in the raspberry crop in Scotland which supplies fruit for the processing industry. The system of raising young plants in standard modules has permitted automated planting machinery to be used when establishing vegetable and salad crops in the field. The use of mobile Brussels sprout harvesters, which strip sprouts from the plant stem with minimal human intervention, has made brassica crops easier and quicker to harvest at a time of year when field conditions can be cold and wet for field staff. The harvested product is now placed into re-usable plastic crates and loaded onto trailers by telescopic handling equipment and transported to the pack-house by fast tractors. When used correctly these developments have had the effect of minimising damage and delay before the product reaches the customer. Research continues to develop harvesting machinery and defect removal systems which will reduce the dependence of the grower on large numbers of field workers. A critical feature of these post harvest handling activities is the emphasis on safety and hygiene to ensure that the harvested materials are free of contamination. Hazards arising from sources such as pesticides, fuels, irrigation water, and human intervention are identified and controlled by adopting good practice in field operations.

2.3 Livestock farming

2.3.1 Background

The livestock sector of the agriculture industry has undergone massive changes in the structure of the business over the past ten years, particularly in the UK. All types of farm have been affected in some way, for example;

- The *Salmonella* in eggs scare in 1989 highlighted some of the hygiene related issues which were to dominate the industry in the following years.
- BSE in cattle led to the reorganisation of arrangements for feeding and slaughter of beef cattle and a collapse in the UK beef export market.
- Animal feed itself became the subject of attention as a result of issues like BSE and the emergence of GM feed crops.
- Concern about the incidence of *Salmonella* and *Campylobacter* on chicken meat and other food products has been an ongoing issue focussing attention on hygienic practices.
- The foot and mouth outbreak in 2001 put many producers of sheep and cattle out of business
- Animal welfare on-farm and during transport of livestock has been an issue, and is now often seen as an 'extended feature' of the product.
- These events increased the need and pressure for extensive traceability and quality assurance measures to be introduced to reassure customers and consumers and to re-establish consumer confidence.

2.3.2 Livestock husbandry

An overview of the operations carried out by livestock farmers in rearing their livestock is depicted by way of a flow diagram in Figure 3.

When purchasing young animals for livestock enterprises, the importance of animal health cannot be overemphasised. Increasingly farmers will obtain animals from herds which can be identified as free of disease and have the records of veterinary inspections to support this. Choice of breeding stock is as important in animal rearing as selection of crop variety is in crop production. Genetics has a significant influence on productivity and the quality of animal products. Selection of desirable traits is highly developed for some species such as pigs, and pig breeding is a substantial and specialised operation. In contrast, many farmers have developed strains of breeds of other animals such as sheep and cattle adapted to particular conditions or even their own farming enterprise. For example, sheep breeds which are adapted to upland conditions, such as the Cheviot or Swaledale, are less suitable for lowland areas (where heavier breeds such as Scottish halfbred, mule and Hampshire Down cross will be better adapted to prime lamb production) but have been used in lowland areas as low cost lamb and for cross-bred ewe production (cross-breds show hybrid vigour - see Glossary).

Buildings used to house stock must comply with appropriate regulations on animal welfare, including clean water supplies and dry bedding if applicable. Intensive pig production involves keeping large numbers of animals in a controlled environment with automatic feeding. Some do not have bedding and will be kept on a slatted floor. Such enterprises can produce lean carcasses in an efficient way. Slurry and manure must be disposed of without contaminating waterways and causing undesirable smell for surrounding areas. Such conditions require a high standard of cleanliness and disinfection of the housing to ensure that there is no build up of disease. In response to animal welfare concerns more pigs, beef animals and poultry are now kept in less intensive outdoor conditions, resulting in slower growth rates and higher feeding costs for these welfare-branded commodities.

Figure 3 - Flow diagram outlining cattle rearing for beef production

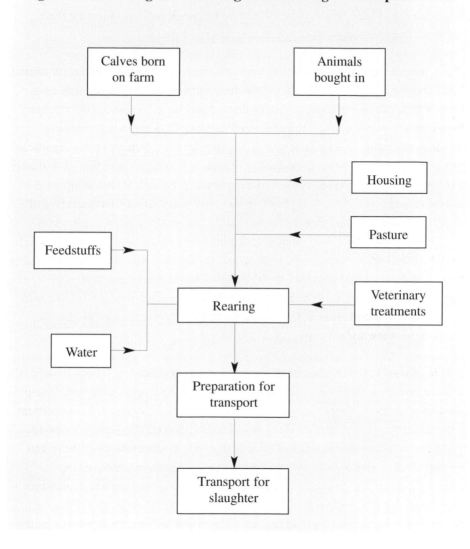

Box 12 - A dairy enterprise: conversion to organic

Shortly after moving to a larger farm and prompted by the opportunity for better returns, Gloucestershire cattle farmer David Haine decided to convert to organic. Being new to the farm meant that conversion should be more straightforward than had it been fully established, and he was already using some of the practices required by the organic system. However, conversion did require change. For example:

- Before conversion the farm held 85 cows and 40 followers (youngstock), together with a 40-head intensive beef unit, all on 53ha of grassland. It produced around 550,000 litres of milk per year (about 6,500 litres per cow). Restrictions on organic stocking density mean that this had to be reduced to 75 cows, 40 followers and no beef unit. Milk production dropped to about 400,000 litres per year (around 5,300 litres per cow). However, the price per litre obtained for the milk through an organic cooperative is steadier and can be anything between 10% and 110% higher.

- All bought-in feed must have either organic certification or, if it is a conventional product (which can be a maximum of 10% feed over a given period), a 'GM-free' certificate. Veterinary drugs can only be used to combat actual problems (i.e. precautionary use is not allowed) and under veterinary authority. Some (e.g. certain hormones) would require prior derogation from the organic certifying body. Man-made fertilisers and pesticides are not permitted and there is a limit on the amount of farmyard manure that can be spread.

- Extensive records have to be kept – for example, on what is fed to animals on an organic/non-organic basis and what is applied to and removed from fields (e.g. manure, hay, silage). A veterinary plan must be maintained, identifying how health problems were addressed, with full medicine/sickness records.

- The certification body (Organic Farmers and Growers) conducts an annual audit on behalf of itself and the cooperative that the farm supplies. This can cover all farm records relating to organic production (including farm accounts), the farm itself and issues such as welfare (which is covered by the National Dairy Farm Assurance scheme – see also Table 8 - p85).

Within a month of deciding to convert, the process was underway. Under the rules of the system it then took 2 years to convert the land and 9 months to convert the stock - though as stock conversion could begin 6 months before the end of land conversion, the total conversion time was $2^{1}/4$ years.

Animal feeds must be provided either as bought in materials which must be manufactured in compliance with animal feedingstuffs regulations or as pasture for grazing which must be free of contamination from sewage sludge or pesticide residues. On mixed farms feed may be grown on farm. The nutritional needs of the animal must match the nutrient value of the feed; this should include protein and energy content as well as micronutrients such as vitamins and minerals. Animals producing milk will have different nutritional needs to animals producing meat or birds producing eggs, and these needs must be understood when formulating diets. Good hygienic practice with respect to feed is important in maintaining disease free stock (see Box 14 - p37)

Animal health needs to be frequently monitored to ensure early recognition of illness, and veterinary medicines used as a preventative measure (vaccination) or to intervene when animals are sick or injured as appropriate. Trained staff must be used to administer medicines and affected animals may need to be segregated. The presence of residues of veterinary medicines in the meat or milk can occur if treated animals are slaughtered or animals are milked before the withdrawal period of the product (i.e. the time between the last administration of treatment and the point at which the animal can be used for food).

A large part of the management of most livestock is the labour required to carry out routine activities such as milking, egg collecting, dipping and supervising movement of stock between fields and buildings. Skilled stockmen will be needed to ensure that these activities are carried out with a minimum of disturbance to the animals. At the end of the rearing process the handling of the animals prior to slaughter may influence the quality of the meat, so attention must be paid to conditions during transport and movement of the animals when they leave the farm.

Box 13 - Eggs: organic, free range, barn and conventional

As alternatives to 'conventional' eggs produced by hens in laying cages, around a fifth of eggs produced in the UK come from barn, deep litter or free range systems. However, about 80% of UK eggs are produced by hens housed in laying cages. In this system three to five birds are kept in a communal cage which provides a minimum area of 450sq cm per bird as set by an EU directive. The feeding, watering and removal of droppings is carried out by mechanised systems. This system allows control of the supply of feed, temperature, water and light, allows good disease control and can suppress aggressive behaviour in the birds.

A small number of hens are kept in barn or deep litter systems. Barn systems are defined by a maximum stocking density of 25 hens per square metre of floor space (400 sq cm per bird) and 15cm of perch space. Deep litter systems are defined by a floor of solid litter of straw or shavings and a density of 7 birds per square metre (just over 1400 sq cm per bird). Both systems must provide one nest box for every 5 birds. Houses must be cleared and disinfected at the end of each laying season.

Birds kept in free range systems produce about 15% of eggs in the UK. Under this system the hens must have continuous daytime access to runs which are covered in vegetation. The maximum stocking density is 1000 birds per hectare (1 per 10 square metre) and the conditions inside the house must comply with the definition of barn or deep litter houses. In free range systems greater freedom for movement and to express natural behaviour such as dust bathing exists but de-beaking is necessary to control aggressive behaviour which arises in large flocks.

2.4 Hygienic practices

The food manufacturing industry has responded to consumer demand for more convenient and fresh foods by supplying a wider range of prepared meals and ready-to-eat products - including the recent trend for minimally processed fresh cut fruit and salad products. Because many of these new products will be eaten without further washing or cooking it is important that they are not contaminated with micro-organisms, chemicals or foreign bodies which might harm or cause illness in the consumer. The presence of small numbers of some bacteria are a potential hazard in such foods. As a result, these manufacturers have implemented

Box 14 - Hygienic design of poultry feed handling equipment

It is well established within food manufacturing that good design of equipment can help to prevent contamination of food products - and this is now being recognised earlier in the food production chain. Good hygienic design of equipment helps prevent growth of micro-organisms, their carry-over between batch-runs and potential post-process re-contamination, by providing fewer opportunities for build up of debris where microbes can breed. By making the cleaning operation easier it can also reduce the costs associated with keeping equipment clean and so create cleaning schedules which are much more likely to be adhered to by personnel.

Hygienic design of equipment used in the post-process production and transportation of poultry feed provides a good example. With increasing incidences of human salmonellosis in the UK in the 1990s, measures were adopted to tackle feed as a possible route for *Salmonella* contamination of poultry - which had itself been implicated as one source of human salmonellosis. For heat processed poultry feeds, ensuring that the heat process is adequate to destroy *Salmonella* goes a long way towards this, but is of little value if the feed is re-contaminated after the process has been administered - for example, during post-process handling, transportation or storage. Examples of the principles of good hygienic design, which can help prevent re-contamination, include:

- Using materials that are suitable for their intended use and which are durable, cleanable, resistant to physical damage (e.g. flaking, cracking, abrasion), non-toxic, non-absorbent and will not release undesirable colours or odours
- Ensuring that contact surfaces are smooth, continuous (or sealed) and easily cleanable (e.g. free of crevices)
- Designing joints so that they have smooth finishes with minimal projections and recesses, and corners which are curved to allow thorough cleaning
- Making sure that fasteners (e.g. screws and bolts) are used only where absolutely necessary and can easily be cleaned / disinfected
- Ensuring that, where wet cleaning is necessary, drainage is adequate for the discharge of cleaning fluids, disinfectants and rinsing fluids, and that there are no dead spaces for the accumulation of debris or trapping of liquids

By addressing these issues at the design stage much can be done to make cleaning easier and more effective and prevent contamination of feed during post-process handling, transportation and storage.

Further reading:

Timperley, A.W. (2000) Heat processed poultry feed: hygienic design of post-process production and transportation equipment. CCFRA Guideline No. 30.

Hutton, T. (2001) Introduction to hygiene in food processing. CCFRA Key Topic No. 4.

high standards of hygiene in the facilities in which these foods are prepared. In turn their suppliers are required to demonstrate that they are following good hygienic practices in the production, harvesting and supply of fruit, vegetable and livestock raw materials which are used as ingredients in such foods.

With increases in the reported incidence of food poisoning cases in many Western countries over the last 20 or so years, the food industry has become much more aware of the critical importance of good hygienic practice in all areas of food production - not just from the manufacturing / processing stage.

One aspect of controlling hygiene issues is a good understanding of the origin and cause of such hazards and the use of measures to prevent and control problems. This is covered in more detail in Chapters 3 and 5 but is mentioned here to emphasise the importance of handling practices. Examples of relevant aspects of production and handling practices in an agricultural situation include:

- Livestock should be sourced from disease-free stock and their disease-free status maintained as far as is possible through the use of good husbandry
- Good hygienic practice should be employed to minimise opportunities for contamination of inputs such as animal feed (e.g. during handling, transport and storage) (see Box 14 - p37)
- Staff should be instructed that they should not work with livestock or handle fresh produce if they have an upset stomach or skin complaint.
- Fresh produce should be irrigated with water which will not contaminate crops with unacceptable levels of micro-organisms.
- Fruit and vegetables should be harvested by staff who have access to adequate toilets and hand washing facilities.
- Stored produce and packaging should be in an environment which is free of infestation by birds and rodents.

Box 15 - Freedom Foods

Freedom Food is an independent assurance and labelling scheme set up by the RSPCA (Royal Society for Prevention of Cruelty to Animals) in the UK. Its aim is to improve animal welfare at every stage from farm to abattoir.

Specific standards have been prepared for all main species of farm animals, including chickens (laying hens and broiler chickens), dairy and beef cattle, sheep, pigs, turkeys and ducks. These have been established in consultation with industry specialists and aim to meet the behavioural and physiological needs of the animal. The standards also incorporate, and exceed in many respects, current UK and EU legislation and Codes of Practice. Traceability is also a key feature of the scheme.

The standards address basic needs of the animals through five freedoms which can be regarded as part of good agricultural practice:

- Freedom from fear and distress
- Freedom to express normal behaviour
- Freedom from hunger and thirst
- Freedom from discomfort
- Freedom from pain, injury and disease.

Any farmer, producer, food manufacturer, haulier or abattoir can apply to join the scheme. Members of the scheme are subject to regular assessments by a Freedom Foods approved assessor, at least once a year.

Further reading:

The RSPCA Freedom Foods website can be accessed from www.rspca.org.uk

2.5 Social and environmental issues

Consumers are naturally interested in the food they eat and are concerned about food related issues. This interest not only relates to eating quality but also to safety and quality issues, including the so called 'extended product' quality issues which relate, for example, to production methods. These production issues take into account general attributes that affect a product's market placing, including environmental and social issues. While price is still the single most significant factor in shaping consumer choice, recent years have seen a marked increase in marketing of the whole 'extended' product.

This issue of the 'extended product' is covered further in Chapter 4 (see p. 77), but examples of how these extended product issues are being addressed include animal welfare standards and the adoption of Integrated Farm Management (IFM). The growing consumer concern about the way in which farm animals are reared has led to greater emphasis on raising standards of farm animal welfare, as exemplified by the RSPCA's (Royal Society for Prevention of Cruelty to Animals) Freedom Food scheme (see Box 15). IFM combines the best of modern technology with the basic principles of good agricultural practice and includes practices that avoid waste, enhance energy conservation and minimise pollution as exemplified by the LEAF scheme (see Box 16). Another approach, which is now being used to assess the environmental impact of specific products and processes, is life cycle assessment (see Box 17).

Box 16 - Integrated farm management (IFM) and LEAF

Many farmers are concerned about the way in which they produce food and are interested in farming in ways that are sensitive to the environment and at the same time financially sound. IFM is a system of farming, which is achievable for the majority of farmers, that combines practical and profitable methods of food production with an awareness and concern for its environmental impact.

IFM has been defined as a whole farm policy providing the basis for efficient and profitable production which is economically viable and environmentally responsible. IFM integrates beneficial natural processes into modern farming practices using advanced technology. It aims to minimise environmental risks while conserving, enhancing and recreating that which is of environmental importance.

The wheel illustrates the various factors taken into account in integrated crop management (ICM) - the application of the 'integrated philosophy' to crops. For livestock systems, animal husbandry would provide an additional cog in the wheel. IFM looks at the whole farm, combining the best of modern technology with the basic principles of good farming practice. It includes practices that avoid waste, enhance energy efficiency and minimise pollution.

LEAF (Linking Environment And Farming) is an organisation in the UK that encourages farmers to adopt IFM. It also aims to promote the benefits of IFM to consumers and raise awareness of the way many farmers are responding to current concerns.

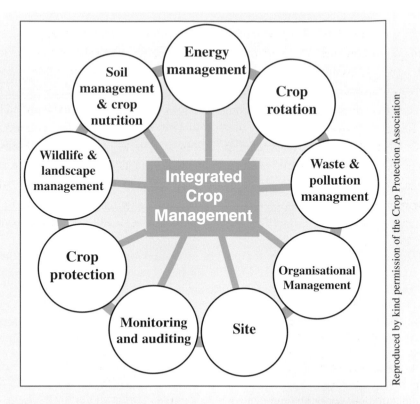

Reproduced by kind permission of the Crop Protection Association

LEAF leads action for farmers in a number of ways, particularly by:

- demonstrating IFM principles on a nationwide network of Demonstration Farms to show other farmers how to adopt it; and
- supporting farmers to take up IFM by providing them with a detailed self-assessment audit of their farm which helps them to set targets to improve their business. LEAF also provides guidelines and other technical information.

LEAF is part of a European wide movement - the 'European Initiative for Sustainable Development in Agriculture (EISA). Similar projects operate in other European countries including Germany, France, Italy, Luxembourg and Sweden.

Further reading:

BAA (1996) Integrated crop management: Crop Protection Association (formerly British Agrochemicals Association). ISBN 0 905598 05 9

LEAF (2000) The LEAF handbook for integrated farm management. See www.leafuk.org

LEAF (2000) Your virtual farm walk CD-ROM. See www.leafuk.org

Box 17 - Life cycle assessment of apples

Life cycle assessment (LCA) is an approach to assessing the environmental impact of a product, service or activity. LCA is an objective approach and can be equally applied to a product of agriculture as to, say, manufactured goods such as TVs and washing machines. Irrespective of the nature of the product, its production is analysed from 'cradle-to-grave' - from the production and use of raw materials right through to disposal of waste when the product has been used.

SIK - the Swedish Institute of Food and Biotechnology - has undertaken various LCAs of food products comparing the impact of similar products that have different systems of production, packaging, transport, storage or retail.

The approach works both for comparative analyses (how does 'process' A compare with 'process' B) and for identifying 'hotspots' - stages in the process which have a particularly high environmental impact.

In one study, SIK conducted a LCA of apples - domestic (i.e. Swedish), European (from France) and 'overseas' (from New Zealand). The 'product' for the purposes of the study was 1 kg of apples and the life cycle was defined as extending from the point at which apple production was established through to delivery of the apple to the store. The study took in factors such as contribution to ozone depletion, generation of greenhouse gases, energy consumption for transport and storage, and impact of pesticides.

Some of the conclusions were perhaps not surprising, but nonetheless interesting as the study illustrates the usefulness of the approach in assessing the true environmental impact of bringing a product to market. For example:

- Higher harvest yields meant that, per kilo, production of the New Zealand apples was more energy efficient than the Swedish or French systems
- Looking at the energy efficiency of the life cycle as a whole, the Swedish apples ranked highest - consuming around half that of the French apples and only one-fifth to one-seventh that of the New Zealand apples
- Energy consumption was dominated by transport (though per kilometre, sea transport was much more efficient than road transport) but storage, in large, energy-efficient cold-stores, was of much less significance
- With regards to pesticides, and reflecting differences in the production systems, the French apples had the greatest impact on aquatic environmental systems while the New Zealand apples had the greatest impact on terrestrial environmental systems.

Overall, the study concluded that domestic product had least environmental impact, but also highlighted areas where the impact of all three systems could be reduced. Although LCA is currently not used to a great extent in food production and manufacturing, it may become a greater consideration in future.

Further reading:

Stadig, M. (2001) Life cycle assessment of apple production: case studies for Sweden, New Zealand and France. SIK Report No. 683 - Swedish Institute for Food and Biotechnology

2.6 Summary

Although the practicalities of handling practices differ widely with different types of and approaches to farming, several features, which are common to them all to a greater or lesser degree, have emerged in recent years. These are discussed in more detail in subsequent chapters but include:

- Closer working relationships between primary producers (suppliers) and their customers - with customers balancing the logistics of production cycles, harvest storage, seasonal supply and international sourcing

- Greater emphasis on assurance of safety and quality - through systems such as HACCP and quality management

- Moves away from highly intensive farming systems towards integrated and, to a lesser extent, organic systems

- Extension of the product beyond its own physical, chemical and biological properties to take in issues such as environmental and animal welfare concerns

Producing food remains, however, a practical exercise subject to the whims of nature and all the problems and variability that nature has to offer.

3. FOOD SAFETY ISSUES

3.1 What are food safety hazards?

Broadly, a food safety hazard is a biological, chemical or physical agent which causes an adverse health reaction in the consumer. Both chemical and biological (particularly microbiological) hazards can occur naturally in primary products and all three types of hazard can potentially gain access during primary production and post-harvest handling of primary products. This chapter focuses on typical food safety hazards of agricultural origin and outlines why they are of concern.

Understanding the nature of the potential hazards that may be present in primary products is important. Current interests in primary products as food raw materials focus on both food safety hazards and food quality issues, but the two should not be confused. Food quality issues are discussed separately in Chapter 4. Some food safety hazards are specifically defined in legislation, customer specifications or adopted codes and guidelines. Others are recognised from previous experience and trading history. Some examples of typical food safety hazards of primary products are shown in Table 3.

Box 18 - Hazard and risk

Hazard and risk are not the same. Although precise definitions vary, the following are useful in making the distinction clear in the context of food production.

Hazard - A biological, chemical or physical property in food with the potential to cause an adverse health reaction

Risk - The likelihood of the hazard causing an adverse health reaction, taking into account the likely severity of that effect.

Table 3 - Typical food safety hazards of primary products

Biological hazards	Chemical hazards	Physical hazards
Food poisoning organisms: e.g. bacterial pathogens, protozoa, viruses	Residues of pesticides and veterinary products	Foreign bodies: e.g. glass, metal, wood, stones
Disease causing agents e.g. BSE prion	Naturally occurring contaminants: e.g. heavy metals (e.g. lead and cadmium), nitrates, mycotoxins, glycoalkaloids	
	Other agricultural contaminants e.g. mineral oils, cleaning chemical residues	

This is not an exhaustive list of hazards of primary products. Some hazards are generic to many primary products (crops and animals included), others may be specific to certain primary products or production operations (e.g. nitrates in lettuce, mycotoxins in cereals).

The actual hazards in a particular agricultural situation, however, will depend on the specific circumstances including the location, production system and intended market. There are numerous theoretical safety hazards in primary products, but only a few will be of significance in any agricultural situation. In deciding the significance of a hazard, the risk associated with any hazard will have to be taken into account, that is the likelihood of the hazard occurring and the severity of the hazard in respect of the adverse health affect. For food safety hazards associated with primary products this may be difficult to judge and factors such as whether there are legal standards or customer requirement may need to be taken into account - that is recommendations from competent authorities.

3.2 Routes of contamination

Awareness and understanding of the possible causes of the food safety hazards in agriculture is important amongst those involved in food production, as this will help them determine the most effective control measures. In addition, the identification of the cause of the hazard may help to determine the risk associated with the hazard.

The majority of food safety hazards on primary products probably arise as a result of being introduced during primary production and/or post harvest handling operations via inputs, people, pests, equipment and the environment. For example, they may be:

◆ associated with inputs in crop and animal husbandry (e.g. manure, irrigation water, animal feeds) or;

◆ introduced by activities associated with people, use of equipment or from the environment (e.g. pest activity post-harvest).

In some instances, contamination may be a result of changes in a pre-existing condition or hazard. For example, certain conditions in the storage of cereals may lead to the production of fungal toxins. Similarly, food poisoning bacteria may grow if the product is not stored correctly (e.g. in milk). In these instances what was not a problem may become one as a consequence of changes induced by the actual production or handling processes.

It should be noted that some quality issues may in the first instance be considered food safety hazards. A typical example is pests, including insects, rodents and birds. These animals do not in themselves cause an adverse health effect but they are important because they can spread disease, that is a they are a potential source of food poisoning organisms. It is the latter that is the safety hazard, not the pest itself.

Examples of some possible causes of the typical microbiological and chemical food safety hazards in crop production are shown in the Table 3.

3.3 Preventing contamination

From a food hygiene point of view, food safety in agriculture is mainly about preventing contamination and preventing the development of hazards. In general, there are few, if any, opportunities in most primary production operations to eliminate or reduce a hazard once it has occurred. There are notable exceptions of course, such as inspection, grading and washing to remove physical hazards in produce.

In general, good agricultural practice is about minimising the likelihood of a food safety hazard arising. The measures for controlling hazards in agriculture can be broadly divided into:

- training of staff - that is, to ensure that staff do their job in a way which minimises hazards
- actions associated with the product - an action as a control measure is the process of doing something specific in the production operation which acts on the product (e.g. temperature controlled storage, drying of grain)
- activities associated with the production process - an activity as a control measure is a policy or procedure associated with the production operation (e.g. pest control procedures)

More than one control may be required to prevent a specific hazard that occurs at different parts of the production process. In the same way, however, one control may prevent more than one hazard at different points in the production process. This is covered in more detail in Chapter 5.

3.4 Micro-organisms of concern

There is a wide range of food poisoning organisms that can potentially contaminate primary products, including bacterial pathogens, viruses and parasites. The vast majority of outbreaks of food-related illness are due to these pathogenic micro-organisms rather than chemical and physical contaminants. Some food poisoning organisms such as pathogenic bacteria can multiply profusely in foods without necessarily altering the food in appearance, taste and smell. This means that something on the raw material that is not a problem to start with, may quickly become one in the food product made from it. The presence of these micro-organisms on raw materials including agricultural products is, therefore, of concern to the food industry. Brief details of some of the more important organisms are given.

Escherichia coli

E.coli is a ubiquitous inhabitant of mammalian intestines including stock animals and humans. There are many different strains of this organisms, the vast majority of which are not harmful. However, some are not benign, including the toxin producing group of which *E.coli* O157 is a member. Doses of very low numbers of the organism can result in illness and the toxin it produces is highly potent. An outbreak in Scotland in 1997 caused illness in around 500 people and resulted in 22 deaths. There have also been several serious outbreaks in other parts of the world including the USA and Japan. *E.coli* O157 can occur in cattle without affecting their health. However, if it contaminates the carcass and then the meat, it can find its way into meat products. It can also contaminate crop products via manure, irrigation water and poor handling (e.g. people and pests). *E.coli* can survive in the environment, animal faeces and soil for extended periods of time (i.e. several months). In fact *E.coli* levels have been used to monitor the quality of irrigation water and hygiene of handling in agriculture.

Box 19 - Safe sludge matrix

The use of raw or untreated sewage sludge on all agricultural land has been phased out in the UK. As a result an agreement was made between the water and sewage operators in the UK and the British Retail Consortium (BRC) representing the major retailers. The Safe Sludge Matrix forms the basis of the agreement and consists of a table of crop types, together with clear guidance on the minimum acceptable level of treatment for any sewage sludge (biosolids) based product which may be applied to that crop or agricultural land. The Matrix enables farmers and growers to continue to utilise the beneficial properties of biosolids as a source of nutrients and as a soil conditioner, whilst at the same time giving the food industry confidence that sludge reuse on agricultural land is safe.

There are a range of different treatment processes used to reduce the possible health hazards associated with sewage sludge. The Matrix gives guidance on the use of these treated sludges on various crop groups, including any conditions that apply. The crop groups cover fruit, salad (i.e. ready to eat crops), vegetables, horticulture, combinable and animal feed crops and grassland and maize (silage and grazing). For example, treated and enhanced treated sludges may be applied to vegetables with 12 and 10 month harvest intervals respectively, whereas these same sludges may be applied to combinable crops without harvest interval restrictions.

Further information can be found at the following website:

www.water.org.uk and www.adas.co.uk

Listeria monocytogenes

This organism has two important characteristics. It has a widespread natural occurrence in the environment, and it can grow at refrigerated temperatures. It is therefore particularly important in chilled foods that are not going to be cooked prior to consumption including salad vegetables and foods such as cheeses and pâtés. Infection with this organism is potentially serious, even fatal, particularly in the young, old or immuno-compromised and in pregnant women.

Salmonella

There are many strains of *Salmonella* which are known to cause food poisoning. They have been particularly associated with poultry and eggs but outbreaks have been associated with a wide range of foods, including salad vegetables and beansprouts (see Boxes 20 and 21). *Salmonella* organisms are widespread in the environment and may be associated with animals and crop products via contamination from feedingstuffs, manure, water and poor handling.

Animal feedingstuffs are acknowledged to be one possible route of contamination of *Salmonella*. The UK government has issued a detailed Code of Practice which provides non-statutory guidelines for establishing good practices and safeguarding the microbiological quality of raw materials used directly as, or intended for incorporation into, animal feedingstuffs, in order that the risk of contamination with *Salmonella* is minimised (see legislation chapter). Similar guidance has also been incorporated into industry schemes including the UKASTA Code of Practice for the storage and transport of cereals and the manufacture of animal feeds.

Campylobacter

Campylobacter is a very common cause of gastrointestinal infection in the UK and worldwide, although it has a much lower public profile than micro-organisms like *Salmonella* and *Listeria*. Many of the reported cases are believed to originate from food. Poultry is one of the most common foods associated with infection. Like many other major vegetative pathogens it is not resistant to heat and is destroyed by

Box 20 - Hygienic bean sprouts

The sprouts of various germinated beans and seeds can be eaten raw or cooked. Being mostly water (90%) with some carbohydrate (4%) and protein (3%), bean sprouts contain very little fat but various minerals and vitamins - including vitamin C which is believed to be synthesised during germination.

In March-April 1988, an outbreak of 159 cases of *Salmonella* (*S. saint-paul* and *S. virchow*) poisoning were attributed to sprouted imported mung beans in England. A similar outbreak occurred in Sweden at around the same time. *Salmonella* contamination of beans was traced to possible cross-contamination from dust from an animal feed mill. The industry was advised by the UK Department of Health to develop a code of practice for bean sprout production.

Steps in mung bean production

Storage of dried beans
↓
Inspection and washing of beans
↓
Soaking and germination of beans
↓
Growth of sprouts
↓
Harvesting of sprouts
↓
Washing of sprouts
↓
Packing
↓
Chilling
↓
Storage and distribution of product

By depicting the mung bean production process as a series of steps (as is now routine with HACCP) it was possible to identify the points at which microbial contamination could arise, develop controls to prevent contamination and microbial growth, and create a check-list of measures to assure product safety. These ranged from appropriate storage conditions and microbiological testing of the raw materials, through appropriate cleaning of containers and equipment and personnel hygiene of packers, to metal detection and chilled storage of the final product and clear instructions to consumers on use and storage.

Further reading:

Brown, K.L. and Oscroft, C.A. (1989) Guidelines for the hygienic manufacture, distribution and retail sale of sprouted seeds with particular reference to mung beans. CCFRA Technical Manual No. 25.

Box 21 - *Salmonella* in eggs and poultry

The "*Salmonella* in eggs" scare is widely seen as the first in a series of major UK food scares emerging from 1988 onwards. It followed a claim by a government junior minister that UK eggs and poultry were widely contaminated with *Salmonella*. In the ensuing debate, particular concern was expressed over *Salmonella* Enteritidis Phage Type 4 (PT4) as it can contaminate eggs if it infects chicken reproductive tissues. The number of food poisoning cases associated with isolation of *S*. Enteritidis from humans rose sharply during the late 1980s and early 1990s - from around 500 isolates in 1981, peaking at over 17,000 in 1993 (POST, 1997).

A two-pronged approach was adopted to tackle the problem of *Salmonella* in eggs and poultry. Firstly, compulsory testing of laying flocks was followed up with slaughter of all flocks found to be infected. This led to the compulsory slaughter of nearly 400 flocks, totalling around two million birds, between March 1989 and February 1993. The second approach was to introduce measures to reduce contamination of poultry feed via a series of codes of practice (see, for example, MAFF, 1989). Typical measures included adopting, implementing and documenting systems to ensure that raw materials and final feeds were of satisfactory bacteriological quality, and that this was supported by appropriate analytical monitoring, personnel hygiene and training, and hygiene of premises and transport systems (MAFF, 1989).

As a consequence of these approaches, the incidents of *S*.Enteritidis in UK domestic fowl has fallen in recent years, mirrored by a fall in the numbers of confirmed isolates from humans (POST, 1997).

Further reading:

MAFF (1989) Code of practice for the control of salmonellae in the production of final feed for livestock in premises producing over 10,000 tonnes per annum. MAFF Leaflet PB 0018.

POST (1997) Safer eating - microbiological food poisoning and its prevention. Parliamentary Office of Science and Technology, ISBN 1 897941 56 0.

proper cooking. However, undercooking of poultry meat might provide perfect conditions for its growth.

The significance of *Campylobacter* is recognised internationally, and in the UK the Food Standards Agency is funding a series of projects exploring different aspects of the biology and epidemiology of this micro-organism. The UK's Advisory Committee on the Microbiological Safety of Food has established a specific working group with the aim of co-ordinating the research, identifying gaps and developing a strategic overview of *Campylobacter* control.

Other bacteria

Other examples of organisms of significance as causes of food poisoning that may be present on primary products, particularly crops, are *Shigella* species and *Vibrio cholerae* (where it is the presence of the organism that is a problem) and *Bacillus cereus, Clostridium botulinum,* and *Staphylococcus aureus* (where the toxins that they can produce are the problem). In general, however, these toxins are not a food safety problem on primary products but may become a problem in manufactured/processed food products.

A number of other pathogenic bacteria can also be associated with livestock, including *Brucella abortus* and *Mycobacterium tuberculosis,* particularly in milk.

Protozoa

Pathogenic protozoan organisms (i.e. which are not bacteria) of concern are the waterborne *Cryptosporidium, Giardia* and *Cyclospora* (which has been associated with soft fruit in the USA). *Cryptosporidium* is of particular concern to the water industry. It is more resistant to chlorine disinfecting than bacterial pathogens. The significance of these organisms in agricultural produce is not clear, but they may be a problem in specific circumstances, particularly if contaminated water is used for irrigation or post-harvest washing of harvested produce.

Viruses

Viruses are an area of growing concern as far as foodborne illness is concerned. They are very simple forms of life and most do not persist for long outside their host (e.g. on primary products) and none can multiply in food. The incidence of food poisoning from viruses is perceived to be fairly small, although symptoms can be quite severe.

In England and Wales, several outbreaks have been attributed to paraviruses, usually involving seafood molluscs, which may accumulate the viruses from organic matter in polluted water. Other viruses which may be associated with crops are Small Round Structured Viruses (SRSV and Norwalk) and Hepatitis A, possibly via contamination from biosolids, water and poor handling. In 1985, for example, several outbreaks of Hepatitis A were traced to frozen raspberries, which were believed to have been contaminated by workers during weighing or picking.

3.5 Chemical hazards of concern

Food chemical safety hazards in primary products may be both 'natural' and extraneous contaminants. Naturally occurring chemical hazards in primary products may not actually be contaminants at all, but natural components of the primary product. Some are of microbiological origin, and while being highly undesirable, are naturally associated with the product. Other chemicals may be used in the production process (e.g. to control pests and diseases in both crops and livestock) or are potential contaminants used in agricultural situations (e.g. mineral oils) or from the general environment (e.g. dioxins).

Current interests in applied chemicals focus on the residues remaining in the product after application in primary production or, in the case of crops, after harvest during storage periods. Other chemicals are adventitious contaminants arising from the environment (e.g. pollutants in the soil, air and water).

Brief details of some of the more important chemical hazards are given in Table 4.

Box 22 - Bovine Spongiform Encephalopathy (BSE)

BSE differs from standard microbiological problems, as it seems to be mediated through an infectious protein - a prion. It is the food scare which has had the single biggest impact on UK public confidence in food safety.

BSE in cattle, along with scrapie in sheep and CJD in humans, is an example of a transmissible spongiform encephalopathy (TSE). Although scrapie has existed in the UK and other countries for over 200 years, the first case of BSE was observed on a Sussex farm in December 1984. In 1992, when the disease reached its peak, there were 36,682 confirmed cases. The origin and transmission of BSE is still the subject of debate. One theory is that BSE has its origins in scrapie, and spread via scrapie and/or BSE-infected material present in cattle feed - possibly exacerbated by changes to the rendering process that eliminated some heat processing and solvent treatments that might otherwise have denatured the infective agent (prion). More recently it has been suggested that the disease arose by chance - as a spontaneous mutation in the prion gene of sheep or cattle in the 1970s - and spread via contaminated animal feed.

The scale of the impact of BSE on consumer confidence is due to the possible link with new variant Creutzfeld-Jakob disease (vCJD) - the human condition suggested to arise from consumption of BSE-infected beef. vCJD emerges through appalling and protracted symptoms, robbing victims of their independence, their dignity and ultimately their life. The lag between infection and emergence of symptoms is believed to be 12-15 years (some suggest it might be as long as 40 years). The biology of the disease is poorly understood, there is no cure and little can be done to alleviate the symptoms. Belief in the mechanism by which the disease is transmitted rests on circumstantial evidence, and even the best informed experts are unable to predict the eventual scale of the problem.

The fact that CJD (including vCJD) currently remains an extremely rare condition - the number of cases in the UK has fluctuated between 80 and 90 per annum between 1997 and 2001, which equates to just over one per million of the population - is, for many, far outweighed by the nature of the disease and the possibility that it might lie latent in an already infected population.

Early measures in the UK to control the BSE epidemic involved widespread culling of infected herds (almost 5 million cattle in the UK between 1996 and 2000), restrictions on the age of cattle sent for slaughter, changes in abattoir practice and the prohibition of feedstuffs containing ruminant material.

The measures, albeit at enormous cost, certainly had the desired effect on incidence of BSE in cattle in the UK; by 2000 the number of confirmed cases had fallen to 1,311. However, earlier official assurances as to the safety of beef and beef products in the wake of these measures were regarded with significant scepticism by many. Confidence was further undermined by the announcement on 20th March 1996, by the UK Health Minister, that the most likely explanation of the cause of 10 cases of vCJD was exposure to BSE-infected material. Later that week, the Chairman of the Spongiform Encephalopathy Advisory Committee (SEAC) [to the UK government] was quoted as saying that perhaps half a million people in the UK were infected with CJD. On completion of the BSE enquiry in October 2000, projections of numbers of possible vCJD cases still ranged from tens to tens of thousands.

For the meat industry, the consequence of the 1996 announcements were profound: many stores and catering outlets stopped selling British beef and the EU's standing veterinary committee voted to impose an indefinite world-wide export ban on British beef and beef products. Although this ban has now been lifted, it is possible that the sale of British beef products will be affected for decades in certain sections of the world community. Meanwhile, cases of BSE have been confirmed on mainland Europe and in Japan, and are being monitored carefully.

References:

BSE Enquiry (2000) BSE Inquiry: the report. www.bse.org.uk

Byrne, D. (2001) BSE in Europe. New Food, (4), 9-13.

Craven, B.M. and Stewart, G.T. (1999) Public policy and public health: coping with potential disaster. In: What Risk? Science, Politics and Public Health. Ed: Bate, R. Butterworth Heinemann pp 222-241.

DEFRA (2001) BSE statistics. www.defra.gov.uk

Department of Health (2000) Monthly Creutzfeld-Jakob disease statistics (October 2000). www.doh.gov.uk/cjd/stats/nov01.htm

Ironside, J.W. (1999) nvCJD: exploring the limits of our understanding. Biologist **46** (4): 172-176.

IFST (1999) Position paper on bovine spongiform encephalopathy (BSE). June 1999 edition.

Table 4 - Examples of potential chemical contaminants

'Natural' toxicants	Extraneous contaminants
Nitrates (e.g. in lettuce)	Pesticides
Mycotoxins (e.g. in cereals)	Veterinary medicines
Glycoalkaloids in potatoes	Feed additives (e.g. colourants in fish)
	Cleaning chemicals and disinfectants
	Mineral oils
	Heavy metals
	Environmental pollutants (e.g. dioxins and PCBs)

Pesticides

There is a comprehensive and complex set of legislative controls in the UK and the rest of the European Union on the use of pesticides and the residues remaining in food (see Chapter 6 for further information). There are detailed controls on how pesticides are advertised, sold, supplied, stored and used. Only approved pesticides may be used, and each approved pesticide can only be used for specific purposes and specified crops. There may also be limits on the amount that can be used on the crop, the stage of crop development at which it can be applied and the minimum time interval between the last application and harvest (the so-called harvest interval). The legislation also provides for other aspects of control on use including the training and competence of operators applying pesticides and those advising or making decisions on pesticide use.

Maximum residue levels (MRLs) are the regulatory mechanisms used for controlling the levels of pesticide residues in food though it is important to understand that they provide a basis for trading and are not safety levels (see Box 23). It is an offence to put into circulation food products containing residues in excess of the prescribed MRL. The setting of MRLs is an integral part of the pesticide authorisation process and there is an ongoing EU programme to set MRLs for all food produce/pesticide combinations. MRLs are also being set for some specific food products, for example in the case of baby foods.

The two main issues for food businesses in respect of pesticide use are not exceeding prescribed MRLs (in the country of marketing) and non-approved uses of pesticides (in the country of production). Everyone in the food chain therefore has an interest in using pesticides sensibly and so keeping residues to a minimum.

Veterinary products

Veterinary medicines are used to treat sick animals or prevent disease in livestock. As with pesticides there is a comprehensive set of legislative controls in the UK and European Community on the use of veterinary products and the residues remaining in food. A key feature of the control of veterinary products is the marketing authorisation which is required before any product may be sold.

These marketing authorisations are granted only after the product has undergone an assessment to establish its safety, quality and efficacy. In many respects the principles behind the control of veterinary medicines are similar to those for pesticides, including for example:

◆ approval for specific uses
◆ setting conditions on the approved use - including withdrawal periods (i.e. the period following the cessation of treatment during which an animal or its products should not be used for food)
◆ setting MRLs.

The MRL is the maximum concentration of residue resulting from the use of a veterinary medicine that is legally permitted or recognised as acceptable in or on food. MRLs are set within the European Community for all pharmacologically active substances used in food-producing animals. MRLs are also set on an international basis by the Codex Alimentarius Commission to achieve world-wide harmonisation. Surveillance for veterinary medicine residues is undertaken by the regulatory authorities in the UK and elsewhere in the EC in order to monitor residue levels.

Box 23 - Pesticide Maximum Residue levels

A residue is any pesticide that remains on the harvested product. This can include the pesticide itself and any specified derivatives such as degradation and conversion products, metabolites and impurities which are considered to be of toxicological significance. Many pesticides leave no trace whatsoever - for example, they are applied to parts of the crop that are never consumed or they break down quickly. During the development of a pesticide, detailed studies are undertaken on how the product behaves in the produce and the environment, including assessments of how quickly it breaks down and into what substances. This is done to make sure that, if a residue is left, it is at a safe level for both people and the environment.

Data are also generated so that the Maximum Residue Level can be set. In practical terms, the MRL is the maximum amount of residue you would expect to find in produce when a pesticide product has been used according to the label instructions. MRLs, therefore, are a check on whether the product has been use correctly - that is they are a trading standard. Although, historically, MRLs were set for these trade purposes, they are now often perceived as a measure to protect human health (see below). MRL setting is, therefore, now an integral part of the pesticide authorisation process, and is included in reviews of older pesticides. Advisory MRLs are also set at the international level by the Codex Alimentarius Commission for commodities traded on a worldwide basis, including crop and animal products.

Some pesticide MRLs in the EU are set at the limit of determination (LOD). This is the lowest concentration of a pesticide that can be quantitatively measured using current routine chemical analysis. MRLs set at the LOD are perceived as an effective zero. Proper use of a pesticide often leaves small traces of residue on the commodity at harvest, and therefore most residue levels are substantive values, above the LOD. However, there are three reasons why the MRL might be set at the LOD:

- Use of a pesticide on a particular crop or in particular circumstances is not supported in the EU
- Scientific data show that the intended use might leave residues that would pose an unacceptable risk
- Scientific data provided show that the intended use leaves no determinable residues on the treated commodity at harvest.

In the first two examples, the MRL is set at the LOD to help ensure that the pesticide is not used illegally on this commodity. In the last example, however, the MRL is set at the LOD to help ensure that the pesticide is used correctly on this commodity. Hence an MRL at the LOD does not necessarily mean that use of that pesticide is illegal.

Surveillance programmes are also undertaken to ensure compliance with MRL legislation in many countries worldwide, both by regulatory authorities and food businesses. These monitoring programmes are often mainly directed towards foods where residues are expected. The EU, for example, has an annual Commission recommendation for member states to monitor certain pesticide/produce combinations. In the UK the monitoring results published have been generally reassuring. Some 70% of the food analysed is free of detectable residues. Where residues are detected these are generally below the MRL and often at very low levels. In only about 1% of the samples have residues been found to exceed the MRL or the sample contained a residue of a pesticide not approved in the UK. In general, even these MRL exceedances have not been high enough to cause any concern for consumer safety.

Pesticides and safety - MRLs versus ADIs

Confusion often arises between MRLs (Maximum Residue Levels) and ADIs (Acceptable Daily Intakes), especially during discussions on safety. The MRL is a legal maximum limit on the amount of pesticide allowed to remain on an agricultural commodity (e.g. fruit, vegetable). It is an offence to exceed this limit. MRLs have been set for a wide range of pesticides - however, they are not, in themselves, safety limits. Rather, they reflect the maximum amount of the pesticide that would be expected if it had been applied in accordance with the terms of its regulatory approval (e.g. time and amount of application, period between application and harvest, crop type) and good agricultural practice.

ADI stands for Acceptable Daily Intake and is an expression of a safety limit. The ADI is the amount of a chemical which can be consumed every day of an individual's entire lifetime in the practical certainty, on the basis of known facts, that no harm will result. It is usually expressed as mg of chemical per kg of body weight. When checking that a residue is safe it is necessary to make allowance for those who might consume a disproportionately large quantity of a food containing the residue in question. Consequently, MRLs are set with the aim that likely intakes will be well within the ADI.

Further information:

MAFF (1992) Food and pesticides. Foodsense Leaflet PB0868. Foodsense, London, SE99 7TT.

MAFF (1999) Annual Report of the Working Party on Pesticide Residues 1999. MAFF Pesticides Safety Directorate. www.pesticides.gov.uk

Mycotoxins

Mycotoxins are a chemically diverse group of harmful compounds with a correspondingly diverse range of physiological effects. Members of a number of different fungal genera produce mycotoxins, including *Aspergillus*, *Fusarium* and *Penicillium*, in a range of commodities, including nuts, dried fruits and cereals. Until recently most of the human health issues have focussed on the so-called 'storage mycotoxins', principally the aflatoxins and ochratoxin A. These are produced mainly as a result of the growth of the mould on the commodity when it is stored incorrectly - usually at too high moisture levels. Aflatoxin can also be a problem in milk if contaminated grain is fed to dairy cattle (see Box 24).

More recently attention has begun to focus on toxins produced by *Fusarium* spp. such as the fumonisins and tricothecenes (deoxynivalenol, nivalenol). In cereals these appear to be produced mostly while the grain is developing in the field, in contrast to the 'storage mycotoxins'. Another mycotoxin that has received recent attention is patulin. This mycotoxin is formed by some strains of the mould *Penicillium expansum* which occurs naturally on some fruits and vegetables but most significantly apples . The major dietary source of patulin is apple juice and following a contamination incident in 1992 the UK Food Advisory Committee set an advisory level of 50μg/l. Since then the UK has conducted a series of surveillance exercises to check that products on the market comply with this level.

EU Regulation No 466/2001 setting maximum levels for certain contaminants in foodstuffs sets limits for mycotoxins including aflatoxin and ochratoxin A. These regulations will help ensure that there are no safety issues in foods arising from contamination with mycotoxins.

Heavy metals

Heavy metals are metals which have a high molecular weight, including, for example, mercury, cadmium, arsenic and lead. Heavy metals are usually toxic in low amounts and are therefore a potential health hazard. Metals can occur in a variety of foodstuffs of plant and animal origin. Mostly, they arise indirectly in foodstuffs from the environment - e.g. they are in soil that the crop is grown in, or

Box 24 - Aflatoxin M_1: a rare contaminant of milk

Mycotoxins are toxins produced by some moulds (fungi). Some, but by no means all of the moulds that grow on food can produce mycotoxins and make the food poisonous. The aflatoxins are a good example. They are produced by the moulds *Aspergillus flavus* (hence the name aflatoxin) and *Aspergillus parasiticus*. If not properly controlled, these moulds can grow on cereal grain, nuts, dried figs and some spices, and produce aflatoxins B_1, B_2, G_1 and G_2. The names B_1 and B_2 reflect the fact that under ultraviolet light these aflatoxins fluoresce blue, while the G aflatoxins fluoresce green.

Of these chemically related toxins, B_1 is the most potent and, if present in feed given to cattle, can be metabolised by the animal to the related aflatoxin M_1. Although M_1 is about 10 times less toxic than B_1, it can find its way into the cow's milk and contaminate the supply.

Whilst natural toxicants like aflatoxins cannot be eliminated from the food chain altogether, much can be done to prevent problems before they arise. For example, it is known that the moulds that produce aflatoxins only grow under certain conditions of temperature and humidity - so that their formation can largely be prevented through appropriate post-harvest storage. Knowing this, companies can build controls into their HACCP plans. Furthermore, legislation specifies limits on the levels of mycotoxin in food and feed susceptible to aflatoxin contamination. In the case of aflatoxin M_1 in milk the EU limit is 0.05 parts per billion (0.05 µg per kg) - ten times lower than the Codex maximum level of 0.5 ppb which, itself, has been deemed safe by FAO/WHO (the Food and Agriculture Organisation and the World Health Organisation).

In the UK, the Food Standards Agency routinely monitors susceptible foods for the presence of mycotoxins. Surveillance exercises of this nature help to ascertain whether legislation designed to prevent contamination is working and will encourage companies to undertake surveillance themselves and to regard the hazard as one worthy of control within a HACCP plan.

In the most recent survey, involving 100 milk samples taken at the farm gate and from retail outlets, and including both conventionally produced and organic milk, FSA found that 97% of samples contained no detectable aflatoxin M1. Furthermore, the levels in the 3% that contained traces of M_1 were well below the limit set by the EU.

Further reading:

FSA (2001) Survey of milk for mycotoxins. FSA Food Survey Information Sheet No. 17/01. Food Standards Agency, London, UK.

Smith, J.E. (2001) Mycotoxins pp238-259 in Food Chemical Safety - Volume 1: Contaminants. Watson, D. (Ed) Woodhead Publishing. ISBN 1 85573 462 1.

on the grass that a cow is eating or in the water in which a fish is living. As such, once they become incorporated into the food they cannot be removed. Control of raw materials is, therefore, the only mechanism for ensuring that levels do not become unsafe.

There is a risk to crops and animals themselves from metals in the environment (e.g. they can kill plants and reduce yields) and to humans from eating crop and livestock products. In addition to those listed above, elements which can be harmful to animals and man include copper, fluorine, selenium and molybdenum. These elements can accumulate in primary products that are otherwise growing satisfactorily but which may still affect animals and man. Lead and cadmium are of particular relevance to crop products as food raw materials. Both serve no useful biological function in humans and are toxic if present at sufficient levels. Lead is a widespread environmental pollutant as a consequence of man's activities (e.g. lead mining, smelting and processing, and burning of fossil fuels); the main route of crop contamination is via uptake from the soil. Most lead in the soil comes from aerial deposition though some comes from sewage sludge spread on the land. Cadmium too finds its way into the soil via atmospheric deposition (again a consequence of its industrial use) and to some extent from sewage sludge. A further source of soil cadmium, though again less than aerial deposition, is phosphate-based fertiliser. Cadmium is a natural constituent of phosphate rock from which fertilisers are produced and although the cadmium content varies, low cadmium phosphate rock is rare.

EU Regulation No 466/2001 setting maximum levels for certain contaminants in foodstuffs sets limits for the heavy metals lead, cadmium and mercury in a range of food products. For these and other metals, there have been recommendations published by various governments as to safe levels. Again adherence to these regulations or recommendations should negate any food safety risk.

Nitrates

In general, nitrates in agriculture are considered more of a hazard to the environment and via water than in foods. However, nitrate intake from water and food has received considerable publicity because of its role in methaemoglobinaemia in infants and reported implication in some types of cancer. Nitrate can be reduced to nitrite under the conditions found in the infant stomach. Nitrite can combine with haemoglobin in the bloodstream, leading to methaemoglobinaemia. Sometimes known as the "blue baby syndrome", this can be fatal. The last reported death in the UK was in 1950 and the last confirmed case was in 1972.

The possible involvement of nitrate in cancer is via its role in the generation of nitrosamines. Nitrosamines are known to be very potent carcinogens and are produced by the reaction of nitrate, when reduced to nitrite, with certain nitrogenous compounds found in proteinaceous substrates. Whilst nitrosamines can be formed in the body, the link between high nitrate exposure and the incidence of cancer is often not clear. However, because of these concerns the European Commission's Scientific Committee for Food (SCF) has set acceptable daily intakes (ADI) of 3.65 mg/kg bodyweight for nitrate and 0.06 mg/kg body weight for nitrite. In the UK, total diet studies commissioned by MAFF concluded that the mean daily dietary exposure to nitrate from all sources was well below the ADI.

Nitrates in food might, therefore, have some adverse health effect but the levels in most crops are not generally considered a food safety hazard. However, as green leafy vegetables usually contain higher levels of nitrate than most other foods, EU Regulation No 466/2001, which sets maximum levels for certain contaminants in foodstuffs, provides for maximum levels of nitrates in spinach and fresh lettuce.

It also specifies that these should be reviewed and, if possible, further reduced. There are a number of factors which affect the levels of nitrates in these crops, including nitrate availability in the soil, seasonal variations and environmental influences.

Other types of chemical contaminants

Other 'natural' chemical contaminants are important only in specific products. One such example is glycoalkaloids in potatoes. Glycoalkaloids are naturally present in potatoes and can result in gastrointestinal disorders if ingested in sufficient quantities. The level of glycoalkaloid present in potatoes can be influenced by a number of

Table 5 - Examples of food safety hazards, possible causes and typical controls in crop production

Example 1 - Food poisoning micro-organisms, especially pathogenic bacteria such as *E. coli* and *Salmonella*

Possible cause	Typical controls
Introduction of pathogenic bacteria from husbandry practices - application of organic manure (e.g. human sewage sludge, animal manure, composts and process wastes)	Good Agricultural Practice (GAP) particularly: - relevant codes of practice/guidelines are followed e.g. the Safe Sludge Matrix for use of human sewage sludge in agriculture (UK) - manures used are suitable for the intended purpose and have been suitably treated/composted where appropriate
Introduction of pathogenic bacteria from husbandry practices - irrigation water applied to the crop	The source of water used for irrigation is of a suitable standard (based on a risk assessment and/or microbial analysis)
Introduction of pathogenic bacteria from people handling the crop product at harvest and during post-harvest handling as appropriate	Personal hygiene standards, particularly: - hand washing and toilet facilities - staff with relevant infectious diseases or conditions are excluded from handling food raw materials
Introduction of pathogenic bacteria from pests (birds and rodents) during post-harvest handling and storage	Pest control procedures particularly: - inspection and treatment of premises to deter and eradicate infestations - premises designed and maintained to exclude pests
Introduction of pathogenic bacteria from plant and equipment	Plant hygiene and housekeeping procedures particularly scheduled cleaning of equipment and premises as appropriate
Introduction of pathogenic bacteria from post-harvest practices - washing water	The source of water used for washing is potable (drinking water standard) and water is filtered if recycled

Example 2 - Pesticide residues (fungicides, herbicides, insecticides and plant growth regulators) - exceeding a Maximum Residue Level or a residue of a non-approved pesticide

Introduction due to incorrect use of pesticides - choice of pesticide and application dose and timing	Decisions on use of pesticides are made by competent/qualified decision makers/advisors All pesticides used are officially approved for use and used in accordance with the conditions of approval and the instructions on the product label (manufacturer's recommendations)
Introduction due to incorrect application technique (in the field and store as appropriate)	Pesticides are applied by competent operators qualified to use the equipment required Pesticides are used according to relevant codes of practice, e.g. the Code of Practice for the Safe Use of Pesticides (Green Code) (UK)
Introduction due to inaccurate application equipment	Pesticides are applied using accurate application equipment which is working effectively, particularly: - planned maintenance of equipment - scheduled servicing and work to remedy defects - calibration of equipment to a set schedule - pre-season and regularly throughout the season
Introduction due to incorrect harvest interval or withdrawal period from store (from last time of pesticide application)	GAP, particularly use of pesticides according to manufacturer's recommendations for minimum harvest interval or latest time of application

factors including variety, exposure to light, pre-harvest stress and sprouting post-harvest. Exposure to light can also lead to the production of chlorophyll, which causes greening. The green pigment itself is not toxic but it may indicate that toxic glycoalkaloids may also have been produced. However, there is no direct relationship between greening and glycoalkaloid production.

There are a number of other extraneous chemical contaminants. Some are associated with production practices (such as feed additives in livestock and residues of cleaning chemicals) whereas others are environmental contaminants.

These environmental contaminants may be materials which are used in agricultural situations - fuel oils and machinery lubricants are typical examples. Contamination with these types of chemical hazard tend to be the result of genuine mistakes or accidents. Other contaminants may be general environmental contaminants such as dioxins, PCBs and radioactivity. The risk of contamination with these hazards is much less easy to define and is outside the control of the primary producer.

Oils are widely used in agricultural situations, and include diesel fuel, heating oil, hydraulic oil and lubricants. There is therefore the potential to contaminate primary products either in the field or in post-harvest handling operations, particularly from leaks or spills from equipment which is being used in association with the crop production process. There are no specific legislative requirements for mineral oils in respect of food products, beyond the general provisions of the Food Safety Act (see Chapter 6). However, the presence of mineral oils on primary products is generally considered a food safety hazard as they may have an adverse health affect. It may also be a quality issues in respect of the introduction of a taint (sensory attribute).

PCBs and dioxins are long-lasting environmental contaminants. They are by-products of fires and some manufacturing processes. The latter are subject to strict environmental controls. Their widespread occurence means that PCBs and dioxins are present in many foods; 95% of all human exposure to these chemicals derives from food. The highest concentrations are in fatty foods such as oily fish. The main sources of dioxins in the diet are from meat and milk. In the UK exposure to these chemicals in the diet has fallen by 75% over the last 20 years. This has reduced any associated health risks.

3.6 Physical hazards of concern

The variety of foreign bodies that have been reportedly found in food over the years is considerable, through the majority are food quality issues (e.g. insects) rather than safety issues. Typical food safety issues in food raw materials are glass, metal, wood, stones and toxic berries, all of which can potentially gain access during primary production, including harvesting, as well as post-harvest handling including storage and transport. Glass, metal and wood are widely used in agricultural situations (e.g. glass lights, metal in machinery and wooden handling containers) and may be present in the agricultural environment as general contaminants (e.g. metal from gun sports). Stones and toxic berries are also likely to come in with primary products as a result of the harvesting operation. These are associated with crops as a component of the soil in the case of stones or as weeds in the case of berries.

Glass is perhaps the most contentious of foreign body contaminants and has been the subject of several incidents of malicious contamination. Slivers of glass in a food can be highly dangerous, as they can cause severe internal lacerations and bleeding. Fragments of glass are very difficult to detect, and so very strict procedures need to be in place to prevent contamination. In simple terms, this means prohibiting glass wherever possible, protecting it where it has to be used (e.g. covering up lighting) and avoiding areas where glass is likely to be present (e.g. near lay-byes where people may park their cars and discard glass bottles). This is often linked to strict breakage and other incident procedures, such as in a glass house environment.

It is a simple fact, however, that some contamination with physical hazards at some time is almost inevitable - because most crops and livestock are grown and reared in open and exposed environments. Efforts, therefore, have to be made to address this not just at the primary production stage, but at every stage in the food processing chain.

3.7 Conclusions

Food is biological material and part of the natural world. There are many agents - microbiological, chemical and physical, some natural and some man-made - that can potentially contaminate food materials and final products. Whilst some of these hazards can be eliminated and/or controlled at a later point in the food production chain, there are others which, if not prevented during agricultural food production, will render the food unfit for human and / or animal consumption. A variety of measures can be and are adopted to prevent this happening, and these are discussed in later sections - especially Chapter 5 which covers quality and safety assurance systems.

4. FOOD QUALITY ATTRIBUTES

The food industry depends on a reliable supply of raw materials of good quality for use as ingredients for manufactured products or as commodities to be packed and supplied to retailers. Quality, however, is a term which is widely used but often poorly defined. In the supply chain it needs to be defined clearly, as it forms an important basis for trade. This chapter discusses the concept of food quality attributes, and uses examples to illustrate some of the factors that can affect quality and the way this can be managed within the food supply chain.

4.1 Food quality concepts

Quality can be good or it can be poor, and in terms of product attributes it can mean suitability for one use or market and not for another. The most widely used concept of quality in terms of food raw materials is 'fitness for purpose' - that is, that the material possesses the required physical, chemical, biological and sensory properties to satisfy a given need. In other words, materials of different quality may be equally suited to their different intended uses. In the food industry this is an essential element of the way in which raw materials are utilised.

Nowadays, however, quality extends beyond the traditional concept based on the physical, chemical, biological and sensory properties of the material, to embrace the issues of the 'extended product' based on production-related issues. These 'extended product' issues take into account the more general attributes that affect a product's market placing - such as organic, free range, animal welfare issues, packaging, environmental considerations, 'ethical trading' and so on. Some of these clearly have an agricultural dimension.

A product quality issue may be defined as something that has an adverse effect on the acceptability of the product to the customer and/or consumer. Most food raw material quality issues focus on the suitability for an intended market including functionality or suitability for a particular use, such as a process or manufacturing operation.

Table 6 - Examples of food quality issues of primary products

Biological issues	Chemical issues	Physical issues
Spoilage organisms: e.g. bacterial/fungal rots and moulds	Compositional attributes: e.g. moisture, sugars, fat, protein levels, nutritional aspects	Foreign bodies: e.g. pests, extraneous vegetable matter, foreign vegetable matter
Genetically modified organisms	Spoilage enzymes	Product defects: e.g. grade, size, damage, bruising
Degree of ripeness		Sensory attributes: e.g. colour, flavour, taints
Susceptibility to chill injury		

As well as the many food safety hazards discussed in the previous chapter, there are many specific quality considerations that have to be addressed by producers and purchasers of primary products in both the fresh and processing markets. These range from physical and sensory attributes of the food to how the food is being produced (the so called 'extended product' issues), and what impact the method has on social and environmental welfare.

4.2 Specifying product quality attributes

The usual way in which the quality of a raw material is defined is by agreement of a specification between the grower and the manufacturer or retailer. In this specification, the qualities of the raw material will be defined and the tolerance for any defects will be stated. If these details are agreed between the two parties then the basis of supply is established.

For many items of fresh produce sold as such, there are European standards. Examples of this include the EC Quality Standards for Horticultural Produce. In addition to providing common standards across the EU, these 'specifications' help to protect the consumer by establishing set requirements for products which are highly perishable. Thus, when a retailer labels a product as Class I, the product must

Box 25 - Specification for dessert apples to be sold fresh

The quality of fresh fruits and vegetables is defined by EC Regulation 1619/2001, which describes the minimum requirements which must be met for each of three categories: Extra Class, Class I and Class II. For apples which are marketed as Class I, for example, the provisions include the following:

- Fruit must be intact, sound, clean, practically free from damage and external moisture and free of foreign smell or taste.
- Shape, size and colouring must be characteristic of the variety.
- Slight defects are allowed on individual fruits provided these do not affect the general appearance.
- Skin defects must not exceed 2cm in length or 1 square cm (for scab infection 0.25 square cm)
- The stalk may be missing but the break must be clean.
- The minimum diameter for large varieties must be 65mm, whilst for other varieties it is 55mm.
- The packed product must be uniform in size, so that the difference in diameter for tray packed fruit must not exceed 5mm and for bulk packed fruit 10mm.
- The tolerance for individual apples not meeting the requirement for quality and size is 10% by number or weight.
- Packaging must be new, clean and of a quality to protect the fruit.

Further reading:

MAFF (1996) EC Quality Standards for Horticultural Produce - Fresh Fruit. Ministry of Agriculture, Fisheries and Food. PB05191.

conform with the definition of Class I laid down in the relevant EC quality standard. An example, with respect to apples, is given in Box 25.

The requirement for different product types within a crop need to be described and agreed for each product. For lettuces, there are general requirements for the leaves to be free of decay, blemish and yellowing, there should be no pests such as aphids or slugs, and the crop must be delivered within a specified temperature range. In addition, the minimum weight of a lettuce may be agreed to accommodate the fact that early season crops will be smaller and lighter than summer crops.

Standards of acceptance of Little Gem lettuce or butterhead lettuce need to be described for each product to ensure that size and weight criteria are met and the required number can be packed into a crate without damage.

4.3 Product quality issues - examples

Example 1 - Potatoes

The quality requirements of potatoes provide a good example of the importance of supplying crops of the correct quality for different markets. The market for 'new' or 'early' potatoes has evolved into a product called 'salad potatoes'. The consumer expects this type of potato to be small, and it may or may not have a set skin: the skin of new potatoes may be scraped off, the skin of a salad potato may be set and would be eaten as part of the cooked product. An important part of the quality of this product type is the texture of the cooked potato, which must be firm and 'waxy'. This waxy texture is obtained by growing a suitable variety that must be harvested at an early stage of maturity when the potato has a low level of dry matter. The season of supply can also be extended to provide 'new ' or 'salad' potatoes from May to September from UK growers. Similar products can then be sourced from countries such as Egypt, Spain, and Italy when the UK season has finished (see Chapter 2).

A market also exists for 'baking ' potatoes. To supply for this market, the size must be large enough for the consumer to use a single potato in the meal. The texture of the cooked potato must be open and floury and dry - this is associated with mature potatoes of high dry matter content. The cosmetic appearance of the potato skin is important; it must be free of blemishes caused by damage and disease, and the tubers must be free of bruising and green discoloration. High dry matter potatoes of this quality are easily obtained by grading the required size from the main crop harvest in September and October each year. To provide such a product during the summer is more difficult - early crops of suitable varieties must be grown to produce potatoes of adequate size early in the season with a set skin.

These needs contrast with those of the processing industry - for production of frozen potato chips for example. For this, potatoes must have a high dry matter content to ensure good texture in the frozen chips. Using suitable high dry matter varieties and harvesting at full maturity will be an adequate strategy. Many customers will specify a minimum length for the chips and this may only be achievable if suitable potato

Table 7 - Examples of uses of potato varieties

Variety	UK harvest period	Uses
Charlotte	July	Salad type
Premiere	August	Chips (early season)
Wilja	September	General and baking
Maris Piper	September	Chips and general use
Pentland Dell	September/October	Chips suitable for fast food
Saturna	October-long term storage	Crisps

varieties with long oval shaped tubers are grown. After harvest, these crops are then stored under controlled conditions to provide continuity of supply for processing factories throughout the year.

In addition, the colour of fried product is influenced by the sugar content of the potatoes. At harvest the sugar content of tubers is low, but if temperatures fall below 7°C during storage, sugar will accumulate as a result of conversion of starch to glucose and fructose. If these potatoes are then used of frying, the high temperature of the oil causes sugars to convert to dark coloured compounds which make the colour of the fried product unacceptable. The sugar content of the stored tubers will also increase if the tubers start to sprout at the end of dormancy - as sprouting accelerates the conversion of starch to sugars. As this happens naturally it needs to be controlled. This is usually achieved by applying sprout suppressing chemicals to the stored crop. The storage conditions of potatoes intended for fried potato products are therefore critical in determining the suitability of the harvest for the intended use.

Interestingly, many potatoes for the pre-pack market for general use are stored at cool temperatures, so that sprout suppressing chemicals are not needed. These potatoes, however, cannot be supplied for processing markets because their sugar content will be too high.

This example illustrates the diverse quality requirements which are needed in potatoes to provide raw material for all end uses. It illustrates that the variety grown, the planting and harvesting schedule, and storage conditions all need to be planned in advance to ensure that the material produced is 'fit for purpose'.

Example 2 - milk

The requirements for quality of milk provide a good example of the stringent quality parameters that apply to a product from the livestock sector. The production and sale of milk is subject to legislation designed to protect public health. Many of the standards to which milk is produced are based on legislative requirements; however, payments to the dairy farmer for milk are also based on quality parameters designed to maintain both hygienic and compositional quality. These include:

- **Added water** - Raw milk supplied to factories or dairies must not contain any added water; this can be verified by a freezing point check.

- **Residues** - There are limits to the levels of antibiotic and pesticide residues permitted in milk. Furthermore, any antibiotic in the milk could kill starter culture micro-organisms used in production of fermented dairy products like yoghurt. However, milking cows are prone to infection by mastitis in the udder, and when this condition has clinical symptoms the herdsman will administer antibiotic to the infected udder via the teat. The use of this type of antibiotic will result in residues being partially excreted in the milk for up to five days. Milk from treated cows cannot, therefore, be marketed until the recommended withholding period has elapsed.

- **Cell count** - When animals are not showing clinical symptoms of mastitis there may be a low level of infection. This can be detected by counting the number of somatic cells in the milk. Background monitoring of cell count in milk from individual herds can indicate the general level of mastitis in the herd and is used as a measure of milk quality for payment purposes.

- **Bacterial count** - The general hygienic quality of milk is measured by Total Bacterial Count (TBC) using a standard method which gives a result in number of organisms per millilitre of milk.

- **Fat and solids** - The composition of milk will be monitored to ensure that it attains minimum requirements and as a basis for payment to producers. Butterfat and solids-not-fat are measured. These components will be influenced by the feeding regime of the milking cows, so will be subject to seasonal variations as cattle move from grazing grass in the summer to indoor housing and fodder rations in winter.

These quality parameters illustrate the importance of quality assurance procedures and quality control tests in ensuring that milk, as a raw material, is fit for the purpose intended.

Example 3 - Wheat

The quality of wheat supplied to the milling industry is monitored to ensure that each consignment of flour despatched to the baking industry has the properties which make it suitable for specific end uses - including bread, biscuits, pasta products, batters, sauces and pastry production. Flour used to make bread must have good quality protein which produces gluten of adequate strength (see Box 26).

When wheat is delivered to a grain store or mill it may be subject to a number of quality tests:

♦   The moisture content of the grain will be measured - this is important because high moisture can lead to premature sprouting of the grain, encourage the growth of moulds with the possible formation of mycotoxins, and encourage the growth of micro-organisms that lead to off-flavours and odours

♦   Tests on protein content and quality will determine the visco-elastic properties of the gluten as it may be damaged when the grain is dried before storage. Protein content should attain 13% (dry matter basis) for breadmaking. Protein quality will also be influenced by the timing of application of nitrogen fertiliser to the crop and by the variety of wheat (see Box 26).

♦   The level of *alpha*-amylase enzyme in the grain can be determined by measuring the viscosity of a gelatinised flour-water suspension. This is known as the 'Falling Number test'. Cereal *alpha*-amylase digests starch. It is formed naturally in grain and increases during sprouting. High levels of *alpha*-amylase (i.e. low Falling Number) indicates that the grain is unsuitable for flour milling. Falling Number is influenced by variety and by delays caused by wet weather at harvest.

♦   Specific weight measurement provides the miller with an indication of grain plumpness and hence the potential flour yield that can be achieved.

Box 26 - Protein content, gluten and breadmaking quality of wheat

Gluten is a proteinaceous material found in wheat dough. The quality of the gluten is critical in determining suitability for breadmaking. It is well established that within a given wheat variety the higher protein contents the greater the loaf volume - and this is where gluten plays its role. During bread production, the yeast ferments sugars to produce carbon dioxide which becomes trapped in the dough matrix to give the bread its characteristic bubble structure. Good breadmaking flours contain a gluten which has a low resistance to deformation, maximum extensibility and minimal elasticity. This helps preserve the bubble structure created during mixing and allows a significant expansion during proving (when the dough is left to rise) and baking.

The protein content and gluten quality is influenced not only by the type of wheat used (e.g. some varieties are better suited to breadmaking while others are better for products such as biscuits) but also by agronomic factors. Application of nitrogen fertilisers, for example, can improve the protein content of flour from breadmaking wheat.

Further reading:

Bhandari, D. (2000) The early prediction of breadmaking quality of grain and its improvement through targeted late application of nitrogen fertiliser. HGCA Project Report No. 219.

Cauvain, S. and Young, L. (2001) Baking problems solved. Woodhead Publishing Ltd.

- Samples are passed over sieves to determine the level of screenings and admixture in the grain. This material must be removed prior to milling.

- The variety of wheat may be verified by an electrophoresis test - this is important because different varieties are suited to different uses (e.g. bread, biscuits).

- Farmers can sell wheat at a premium price if it meets minimum requirements for these quality attributes.

Box 27 - Livestock diet and meat quality

Livestock diet can have a marked effect on the composition, quality and shelf-life of meat. Manipulating the diet provides opportunities for improving these properties. For example, the ratio of polyunsaturated to saturated fatty acids in pig meat can be increased by increasing the level of polyunsaturated fatty acids in the animals' diet. This can be achieved by including in the feed materials such as linseed or fish oil, good sources of polyunsaturates. However, this also increases the susceptibility of the meat to oxidation which can lead to the formation of off-flavours and undesirable colour changes. This can be overcome by also increasing the level of vitamin E in the diet. Vitamin E is a natural anti-oxidant and its level in the diet can be increased by including a natural source (e.g. fresh grass has a relatively high level) or through vitamin E supplements which are relatively low cost. This combined can therefore yield meat which has improved fatty acid content but is less prone to oxidative spoilage.

Further information:

Meat & Livestock Commission (2002) Shelf-life of fresh meat: matching product life to requirements. Published by the Meat & Livestock Commission, Milton Keynes, UK.

4.4 Extended product quality issues

In the developed world there is plenty of food, it is generally safe, the cost is low due to efficient production practices, the quality is consistently good and most products are available throughout the year. As a result consumer attention has turned in recent years to how the food is produced, particularly how the food is produced on the farm and growers' holdings. In some ways, this is the most visible part of the food chain as agriculture is all around us in the countryside and, it must be said, some food safety issues have been associated with primary production practices (e.g. pesticide residues, food poisoning and BSE). Consumers are, as a result, questioning what impact the method of primary production has on social and environmental welfare.

An obvious example of this is the rise in the market for organic products, but other issues such as animal welfare, fair trading, environmental protection and even the sustainability of modern agricultural systems are increasingly important. Another example is the issue of GM foods (see Box 29 - p80).

Box 28 - The market for organic products

It is well known that the volume and value of sales of organic foods has been increasing dramatically in recent years. Between 1995 and 2000, the value of UK organic retail sales has more than trebled from £150m to over £500m. In 1997, CCFRA's product intelligence unit identified just 34 new organic food products while the figure for 1999 was 567 (see graph) - this level of growth in product launches reflects the commercial significance of the organic issue to food companies.

Initially consumer interest in organic products centred on fresh produce, but subsequently it expanded to include meat, milk, and a wide range of baked products and manufactured foods. In the UK, the market is supplied by only 30% of raw material from home production - the rest has to be imported. Within the many food sectors the greatest increase in consumption has been the sales of organic baby and infant foods, which account for more than 6% of total sales. This is true also in some other European countries - in Germany for example, organic baby foods make up 60% of the market.

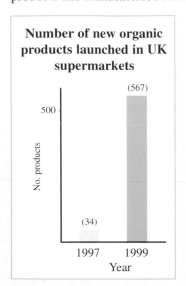

Number of new organic products launched in UK supermarkets

In the UK, major manufacturers of conventional foods are now also organic food producers. In addition to retailer own-label products, manufacturers like Heinz, Mars, and RHM have their own an organic product range and fast food companies such as McDonalds are also now selling organic products in some regions of Europe.

The industry has risen to this challenge and a number of specific regimes and protocols have been introduced in recent years which cover production issues.

Some of these, together with the associated logos, are now widely used as marketing tools. Organic production is a good case in point, but others, such as the little red tractor in the UK (see Chapter 5), free range, the lion egg mark in the UK and dolphin-friendly fishing are in a similar vein.

Many of the production issues are also covered in other specific regimes and protocols that have been adopted by the industry, such as Integrated Crop Management and animal welfare. Some of these are less readily identifiable in marketing terms but have been taken up by the industry as part of a general framework for Good Agricultural Practice in different sectors. These protocols define the essential elements for best practice for agricultural production taking into account the different production issues including social and environmental welfare. The EUREPGAP Protocol for Fresh Fruits and Vegetables, for example, has sections that cover the actual production as well as associated issues such as waste and pollution management, recycling and use, worker health, safety and welfare and environmental issues. Production issues and specific regimes and protocols are discussed further in Chapters 2 and 5 respectively.

Another extended product quality issue is that of 'food miles' - the large scale transportation of food, and its associated financial and environmental cost (e.g. fuel consumption, pollution, traffic congestion). Developments like the re-emergence of farmers' markets are one sign of increased interest in locally produced food. However, as discussed in the Report of the Policy Commission on the Future of Food and Farming this is not a feature of agriculture but of supply chain structure and management with various suggestions proposed for addressing the seemingly conflicting priorities of centralised management of supplier quality/safety assurance and local sourcing of produce and products (see Curry, 2002).

4.5 Product range and consumer choice

Recent trends in food retailing have seen an ever wider range of products on the retailer's shelf. The consumer is given an extended choice of product types from which to choose and this has created market opportunities for the agriculture and horticulture industry. These opportunities take the form of supplying a product over a longer season, or supplying different product types within a cropping system. For example, the diversification of products within the market for leafy salads has developed a need for suppliers of many different types of lettuce - markets for these did not exist a few years ago. Each of these must be supplied to a strict specification regarding, for example; size, weight, colour, trim, temperature and time of delivery.

The increased range of potato types has already been discussed and illustrates how early and salad types and baking potatoes are now available over a long period of the year. Contracts to supply speciality crops out of season provide new opportunities but demand a specification which may only be met by specially planned cropping.

Many of the products offered to the consumer are now available with an organically grown alternative, which has created a market to supply organic foods that sees demand exceeding supply in the UK for many commodities.

Box 29 - Consumer attitudes to food related issues

Consumer awareness, perceptions and attitudes to food related issues is an increasingly important consideration in the supply and marketing of foods. All sectors of the food chain, including the agri-food sector which is where many of these concerns are focussed, need to be aware of the current concerns and respond to them. Research at CCFRA, for example, has been investigating the consumer view on food related issues with special reference to the awareness of and attitudes to organic foods and genetic modification (GM).

The research has shown that consumer perceptions of what organic really means has led to beliefs in improved safety, taste and healthiness of organic produce, which have become some of the main drivers for purchase. For non-purchasers attitudes to organic food were similar with the main obstacle to purchase being price.

The results of the research on GM reveal certain confusion over GM technology. The lack of trustworthy information is apparent. For many the perceived risks particularly of health and safety outweigh the benefits, but the majority of respondents were in favour of further work to investigate the long term impact of GM technology.

Further information:

Newsholme, H.C., Wright, L.J. and McEwan, J.A. (2001) Consumer awareness of and attitudes towards genetic modification. CCFRA R&D Report No. 142.

Newsholme, H.C. (2001) Consumer awareness of and attitudes towards organic foods. CCFRA R&D Report No. 149

5. QUALITY ASSURANCE OF FOOD RAW MATERIALS

Food safety is a shared responsibility. All sectors of the food chain must take responsibility for safeguarding the food supply, as must the consumer during domestic handling, storage and preparation. This has led to the term 'from farm to fork'. As an integral part of the food supply chain, primary production cannot be taken in isolation from other aspects of the food chain. Primary production is, therefore, increasingly subject to the same legislative and market influences as other parts of the food chain in respect of food safety, legality and quality. As a result, primary producers must increasingly satisfy their customers that their products are safe to the consumer, of the required quality and produced to relevant standards.

As has been described in previous sections, there are many safety and quality issues that the food industry has to address. As well as the individual safety hazards or quality issues associated with primary products, the method of primary production is of increasing relevance to the supply of food raw materials. Much time and thought, therefore, needs to be put into the overall management of the production system, particularly with regards to issues of quality assurance and quality control. Quality assurance is the philosophy of setting up management controls to assure that the end product is of the desired 'quality'. In contrast, quality control focuses on retrospective testing of a raw material or product. In recent years there has been a huge shift in emphasis towards preventative quality assurance systems rather than 'reactive' quality control systems, though quality control still has an important role to play and can complement and support quality assurance. One good example of this is in pesticide residue testing to check that the appropriate assurance systems are working.

The increasing integration and sophistication of the food supply chain has led to the emergence of various quality assurance systems, including, for example,

- specifications defining quality of raw materials and products
- production standards and quality assurance schemes defining good practice
- food safety systems based on HACCP principles
- product identity and traceability systems

With the emergence of different systems to assure various aspects of product integrity (encompassing quality and safety) it can be difficult for the user to appreciate how they fit together. This can be quite important in minimising duplication of effort, where different systems address closely related issues. 'Framework' quality management systems have been developed to address this. With regard to primary production, CCFRA together with the British Standards Institution (BSI) developed a framework system, published by BSI as a Publicly Available Specification (PAS). The system applies to those aspects of food safety, quality and production over which the company wishes to demonstrate its control. It helps the user to identify the issues that should be addressed through a quality management system and allows them to call upon information already developed for regulatory or customer-based purposes – including, for example, risk assessment, hazard analysis, specifications and traceability systems.

In this way different elements in the food chain work together to meet the demands and expectations of their customers and ultimately the consumer. In this chapter each of these quality assurance systems is considered in relation to the production of food raw materials together with consideration of how food businesses control their raw materials.

5.1 Specifications

Quality is a widely used term. Quality can be good or it can be poor and in terms of raw material it can mean suitability for one use and not for another. The most widely used concept of quality in terms of food raw materials is 'fitness for purpose' which relates to the ability of the product to satisfy a given need. This may be defined as the relative value of several characteristics of a product which determine the overall acceptability of the product to the buyer and ultimately the consumer. Product quality can be defined in great detail, for example in a specification.

Raw material quality can be assessed by many parameters depending on the requirements of the buyer, including physical parameters (e.g. defects, size and shape), composition characteristics (e.g. dry matter, sugar content) and sensory attributes (e.g. colour, flavour). The individual quality characteristics can be numerous and their relative importance will differ with the product and intended use.

Box 30 - Examples of CCFRA raw material guidelines

CCFRA, in partnership with industry, developed a series of guidelines that provide guidance on general quality of raw materials, how to sample for defects, definitions of what constitutes a defect, permitted levels of defined defects and tolerances on the stipulated levels.

Examples of CCFRA Raw Material Guidelines include:

- Carrots for slicing, dicing and julienne cuts
- Swede and turnips for dicing
- Green beans
- Onions for slicing and dicing
- Brussels sprouts
- Cauliflower florets
- Cabbage for shredding

Freedom from defects is often of paramount importance. This includes freedom from the ravages of pests and disease. More specific defects include, for example, the presence of foreign bodies such as stones, toxic berries and insects, the presence of extraneous vegetable matter, blemished off-coloured and damaged produce and off-flavours and taints.

Specifications may either be voluntary, that is agreed between the supplier and end user as part of their trading arrangements, or government-backed. A voluntary specification in particular is a method which quantifies product quality by combining the objective factors related to the product with the subjective factors related to the user. Voluntary specifications are perhaps the most widely used in the food supply chain and these may refer to any statutory standards where applicable. As an independent organisation CCFRA has worked with food companies to develop a whole series of generic quality specifications for raw materials (Box 30) and for final product (quick frozen and canned products). These are consensus documents drafted and trialled by working groups from industry and published by CCFRA. Similar types of specification are used for materials for processing - such as imported beans for baked bean manufacture (see Box 31).

In some countries, standards are drawn-up by government departments and sampling is carried out by government inspectors to check conformance. In the European Community, for example, there are statutory quality grading standards for a range of produce including fresh fruits and vegetables.

Box 31 - Dried bean specification

Typical requirements in a specification are illustrated by considering the requirements for dried pea beans which are the raw material for manufacture of canned beans in tomato sauce (i.e. 'baked beans'). These are usually grown in North America and shipped to the UK. Control of raw material quality is improved by the use of an agreed specification. This would typically cover the following details:

* A description of the grades which are defined by the specification (e.g. A, B, C)

* A description of the method of ascertaining the grade

* The method of sampling and statement at what point the sample should be taken and the size of the sample required for assessment

* A description of defects - Definition of critical contaminants (e.g. glass, metal, toxic berries)

* Definition of major contaminants (e.g. dead insects)

* Definition of minor contaminants (e.g. vegetable matter)

* Definition of defects (e.g. serious blemishes, ingrained dirt, staining)

* Significance of sprouting beans - evidence of germination

* Significance of insect damage - evidence of insect attack

* Significance of dirty beans - adhering soil

* Significance of mechanical damage (crushed and broken beans)

The definitions and statements will be followed by a description of the tolerance for each of these defects in each grade described. By careful examination of samples of a consignment of raw material, a grade for the consignment can be awarded.

5.2 Production standards and quality management schemes

Regulation in agriculture is a mixture of statutory legislation and industry self-regulation (see Chapter 6). Self-regulation usually comprises the adoption of specific regimes developed by industry or recognised quality management systems developed by international standards bodies. The adoption of these schemes by businesses is voluntary but they may also be a condition of supply for some purchasers of primary products - that is a commercial rather than a legislative requirement.

Table 8 - Examples of specific regimes in the agri-food sector in the UK

Cereals, oilseeds and pulses:	Assured Combinable Crops Scheme (ACCS)
Fruit, vegetables and salads:	Assured Produce (AP)
Beef and lamb:	Farm Assured British Beef and Lamb (FABBL) Farm Assured Welsh Lamb (FAWL) Northern Ireland Farm Quality Assurance Scheme (NIFQAS)
Dairy products:	National Dairy Farm Assured Scheme (NDFAS)
Chicken:	Assured Chicken Production
Pork:	Assured British Pigs
Organic production:	UKROFS Standards for Organic Production Soil Association Standards for Organic Food and Farming
Animal Feed:	UKASTA* Feed Assurance Scheme
Whole Farm:	Linking Environment and Farming (LEAF)
Genetically Modified Organisms (GMO)	BRC/FDF* technical standard for the supply of identity preserved non-genetically modified food ingredients and product

UKASTA - United Kingdom Agricultural Supply Trade Association
BRC - British Retail Consortium
FDF - Food and Drink Federation

In addition to general management philosophies, as exemplified by the ISO 9000 series of quality management standards, there are specific regimes and protocols that are now standard industry practice which apply specifically to different primary production sectors. These specific regimes have been widely adopted by the agricultural industry in the UK. A specific regime or quality assurance scheme is generally comprised of two elements:

- a best practice protocol, that is a 'how-best-to-do-it' instruction or guideline;
- a mechanism for constant surveillance, both internally (self-auditing) and/or through inspections by independent third parties.

There are many examples of these specific regimes, including quality assurance schemes, for primary production world-wide. The scope of these regimes is often specific to a particular sector (e.g. crop or livestock type) or production issue (e.g. organic or GM free). The majority are national but some are becoming internationally accepted - at least by companies exporting to markets where a specific regime is established. Some examples of specific regimes in UK agriculture are given in Table 8.

The Assured Produce Scheme is a typical example of an assurance scheme. It is a UK based scheme for produce (fruits, vegetables and salads including potatoes). There is a protocol for each crop covering crop husbandry, operational controls and environmental management. These protocols are guidelines for best agricultural practice based on Integrated Crop Management (ICM) principles. The surveillance procedures involve an annual self assessment questionnaire (i.e. internal audit) and periodic inspections by external independent verifiers. The scheme was developed and is administered by the industry, including the National Farmers Union and major retailers. The protocols have been prepared by experts and are revised periodically to keep them up to date so that they fully reflect current good practice.

Through the British Farm Standard initiative (the little red tractor), the use of assurance schemes and the benefits they help to deliver can be exploited in the marketing of the end product (see Box 32).

Box 32 - The little red tractor

The 'little red tractor' that now appears on the label of many food products in UK supermarkets and small independent shops was developed to symbolise that the product is produced to British standards of food hygiene, environmental care and animal welfare. In short, it confirms that the product complies with the British Farm Standard. It does not necessarily mean, however, that the product is British. The use of the trademarked logo is managed by Assured Food Standards (AFS), an independent company established to do this: the logo can only be used with the approval of AFS, which is granted via an annually renewable licence.

The logo was launched on 13th June 2000 and initially used for fresh products. In August it was used for the first time for processed vegetables (when it appeared on frozen peas) and in February 2001 it appeared on qualifying processed meat packs (sausages and burgers) and milk.

Market research by the National Farmers Union on the first anniversary of the scheme's launch, conducted to assess its impact, suggested that 1 in 3 of the population were familiar with the logo and that it was popular with both consumers and retailers. However it also identified that further work was needed to promote the fact that the products carrying the logo, and the systems to produce the products, were subject to specified standards that are independently inspected.

So, how does AFS ensure that the approved products and systems meet the required standards? Rather than introducing further quality assurance systems, AFS works with existing assurance schemes - including those for beef and lamb (e.g. FABBL, FAWL and IFQAS), pig meat (ABP), chicken (ACP), dairy (NDFAS), cereals, oilseeds and pulses (ACCS), and fruits, vegetables and salads (AP) (see Table 8, p85 for a list of these schemes). By virtue of their own requirements, these schemes can be used to determine whether a particular product complies the requirements, but further capitalising on work already being undertaken.

Further information:

NFU (2000) A year in the life of the little red tractor. Report of research by the National Farmers Union into consumer and industry response to the British Farm Standard initiative. Visit http://www.nfu.org.uk

The Little Red Tractor Website: www.littleredtractor.org.uk

Whilst the UK industry has been at the forefront of the development of specific regimes and protocols in agriculture, similar developments are now taking place internationally. The Euro-Retailers Produce Working Group (EUREP) was formed to develop a European good agricultural practice (GAP) protocol for fruits and vegetables. The current EUREPGAP Fruits and Vegetables protocol has been developed with input from all sectors of the fresh produce industry including producer organisations outside the European Union. Growers can now seek EUREPGAP approval through independent verification from an independent verification body that is approved by EUREP.

The EUREPGAP document sets out a framework for GAP based on best practice for the production of horticultural products. It defines the minimum standards acceptable to the leading retail groups in Europe. GAP is identified as a means of incorporating Integrated Pest Management (IPM) and ICM practices within the framework of commercial agricultural practice. EUREP is also adapting the principles of GAP as defined in the fruit and vegetable protocol to other agricultural sectors including combinable crops (e.g. cereals, oilseeds and pulses), flowers and ornamentals and animal feed.

5.3 Food safety systems

The internationally recognised philosophy for assuring food safety is HACCP (Hazard Analysis and Critical Control Point). In the UK, HACCP-based systems are well established amongst processors and manufacturers and are now being introduced in all parts of the food supply chain - some primary producers are now using this approach for food safety control. There is no legal requirement for farmers to use the HACCP technique for primary production. However, some post-harvest activities on-farm may be considered food business operations and in these circumstances the implementation of HACCP may be very appropriate.

Currently (2002), proposed EU legislation on the hygiene of foodstuffs will require primary producers to monitor hazards to food safety and to eliminate them or reduce them to an acceptable level. The HACCP approach is an effective method of achieving this.

The HACCP system is based on seven principles, and when conducting a HACCP study in agriculture the seven principles of HACCP may be applied as twelve stages as shown in Table 9. These include both essential preparation tasks (the 'Planning' stages 1 to 4 described here) and the principles of HACCP (the 'Application' stages 5 to 12).

Table 9 - Stages in a HACCP Study in Agriculture and Horticulture

Stage 1 Define the terms of reference

Stage 2 Select the HACCP team

Stage 3 Describe the essential product characteristics

Stage 4 Construct a flow diagram

Stage 5 List all potential hazards associated with each process step, conduct a hazard analysis and consider any measures to control identified hazards (*Principle 1*)

Stage 6 Determine Critical Control Points (*Principle 2*)

Stage 7 Establish critical limits for each CCP (*Principle 3*)

Stage 8 Establish a monitoring system for each CCP (*Principle 4*)

Stage 9 Establish a corrective action plan (*Principle 5*)

Stage 10 Establish verification procedures (*Principle 6*)

Stage 11 Establish documentation and record keeping (*Principle 7*)

Stage 12 Review the HACCP plan

Box 33 - Typical hazards and controls from wheat and beef production HACCP studies

Although production of wheat and beef cattle are completely different operations, HACCP can be applied equally to both. It can be used to identify hazards, determine control points, establish limits, monitor against these, plan remedial actions in the event of a problem and keep records. HACCP is a generic framework that can fit all processes. This small extract from each of two example HACCP analyses illustrates this.

	Common hazards	Typical control measures
Wheat	Introduction of pesticides due to inaccurate application equipment	Equipment is used according to manufacturer's instructions (planned maintenance and calibration to set schedule)
	Introduction of pesticides due to incorrect harvest interval (from last time of application)	Pesticides are used according to manufacturer's instructions for minimum harvest interval
	Introduction of food poisoning organisms from pests (birds and rodents) during post harvest handling and storage	Pest control procedures, including inspection and treatment of premises to deter and eradicate infestations
	Introduction of glass from post-harvest environment	Glass policy, particularly protection of lights, covering of loads in transport and breakage procedures
Beef cattle	Introduction of veterinary residues from veterinary products	Use of approved products, at correct dose rates and adherence to correct withdrawal period
	Introduction of veterinary residues from feed	Use of approved feeds, adherence to correct feeding rates and correct separate storage (from unmedicated feeds)
	Introduction of food poisoning organisms from other herd members during rearing	Adherence to good agricultural practice including suitable stocking densities and veterinary treatment where appropriate
	Introduction of food poisoning organisms at transport to the abattoir	Adherence to clean livestock policy including pre transport cleaning if necessary

Reference:

Bedford, L. and Knight, C. (2001) HACCP in agriculture: livestock. CCFRA Guideline No. 33. Supplement 1: Rearing cattle for beef.

Knight, C. and Stanley, R.P. (1999) Assured crop production: HACCP in agriculture and horticulture. CCFRA Guideline No. 10. Supplement 3: Wheat case study.

Although HACCP has historically been used for assuring food safety, the HACCP technique is now also being used to help assure product quality. It is important, however, that the objective and scope of the system is clearly defined at the outset and that the system is carefully managed to ensure that food safety is the principle objective. There is no doubt that the HACCP technique is a potentially powerful management tool for identifying, evaluating, controlling and monitoring hazards which are significant in primary production, whether they be food safety or other important attributes. In addition, HACCP can and does interface with other quality management systems such as ISO 9000.

The are numerous publications about the philosophy of HACCP and software programmes to help companies formulate and record their HACCP systems. Of particular relevance to primary production are a series of guidelines published by CCFRA on HACCP in agriculture as it can be applied in crop and livestock production (see the section on further reading - p123).

5.4 Traceability

Traceability is an important feature in the food chain including the agri-food sector. Traceability of raw materials is necessary in order to establish that controls have been applied and verify that they are effective and if not establish corrective actions in terms of re-establishing control and dealing with any non-conforming product. However, it should be noted that traceability does not by itself control anything in terms of food safety and quality and cannot prevent or eliminate a safety hazard or reduce it to an acceptable level

Requirements for traceability have been a long standing feature of industry self regulation. Explicit legal demands, however, have been more limited. Current legislation associated with traceability in the EU relates to specific issues, including beef labelling and genetically modified materials. In future, however, food and drink companies may be obliged to ensure traceability under proposed European Commission proposals for the consolidation and simplification of EC food hygiene legislation.

Box 34 - The beef labelling scheme and traceability

Compulsory beef labelling in the EU applies to all fresh and frozen beef and veal at all stages of the production chain from slaughter house to retailer. In the UK this supplements a voluntary beef labelling system that has been in operation since 1998.

The compulsory system, in operation since September 2000, requires full traceability of beef throughout the supply chain. Beef is required to be labelled with:

- a reference code linking meat to the original animal or group of animals from which the meat is derived;
- the country of slaughter;
- the country of cutting.

Claims about the origin, production methods or characteristics of beef which are not compulsory can be made under the voluntary Beef Labelling Scheme.

The overwhelming majority of beef sold in England has labelling indications under the Beef Labelling Scheme. The Scheme requires operators to establish a traceability system and to employ a government recognised independent third party to verify the information on the label. Traceability is the key requirement of the Scheme.

DNA technology can now be used to support and help enforce traceability schemes. The principle is similar to genetic fingerprinting of humans (see Jones, 2000 for more on this); as the DNA is the same in different tissues from an animal (e.g. muscle, kidney) it is possible to identify meat from any given carcass using the technology. In Ireland, IdentiGen recently announced the development of a fingerprinting system called TraceBack™ and its implementation by the retailer Superquinn.

Further reading:

UK DEFRA website: www.defra.gov.uk

IdentiGen website: www.identigen.com

Jones, L. (2000) Molecular methods in food analysis: principles and examples. CCFRA Key Topic in Food Science and Technology. No. 1.

In general, the legislation and industry self-regulation governing traceability is not prescriptive in respect of the specific requirements for traceability - they just define the overall objectives. The specific methods of traceability to be adopted and level of traceability that is achievable will depend on various factors, which relate to the nature of the product and production process under consideration. There are of course exceptions but these relate to specific issues or products. Boxes 34 and 35 outline traceability of beef and crop products respectively.

Traceability features the establishment of the identity, history and source of a product and needs to be established at all stages of the food chain, starting with primary production and the agri-food chain. This means that at each stage operators should be able to identify the nature and source of any materials supplied to them, trace the product up and down the place of production or handling, and identify to whom the product has been supplied. In addition, this information needs to be made available on demand.

The food chain is potentially complex and the type and level of traceability that is achievable depends on various factors, which relate to the nature of the product and production operations undertaken. That is, there is no single system of traceability; it will depend on the scope of the system and what is practicable for a given product or production operation. The system in place should be the most appropriate for the specific circumstance, and should be sufficient to enable the product to be identified to allow a defined supply chain. This is perhaps most marked in primary production and the agri-food supply chain in respect of the supply of primary products.

In the agri-food chain, direct traceability of primary products is feasible for some production systems but not for others - for example, where bulking or mixing are routine at harvest or during post-harvest handling of the primary product, including storage, transport and marketing. Where mixing is practised, the identification of the source materials is paramount in order to establish the assured supply chain - that is, at each stage the materials which contribute to the bulk can be identified, even if physical traceability of the individual lots is lost. A good example of the importance of this was demonstrated by the emergence of a traceability system for soya (see Box 36).

Box 35 - Degrees of traceability of crop products

Traceability of product, or batches of product, right along the food production chain has become much more important as the chain has become more complex and as customers and consumers seek greater assurance of safety and quality. If there is a problem with a product, tracing the source of the material concerned can help to isolate (and/or recall) the affected products, to identify the cause of the problem and to prevent a recurrence.

Direct traceability of primary products is feasible for some production systems but not for others. In the case of lettuces, for example, which can be harvested and packed in the field, individual items can be traced to a defined crop and harvest. This means that information on inputs associated with the end product, including seed, pesticides, fertilisers and irrigation, can be obtained. This situation is analagous to beef traceability (see Box 34).

At the other extreme, and taking a seed crop such as wheat as an example, bulking or mixing is routine after harvest and during storage and marketing. Traceability of individual product is not therefore feasible, but identification of the particular harvested lots that make up a given batch of grain can be possible - so that source can be traced to a 'pool' from a harvest.

Somewhere between these extremes lie crops like potato, where the level of traceability achievable depends on the method of post-harvest handling. For boxed stored crops, it might be possible to trace individual boxes to a defined crop harvest (and again to ascertain the inputs used and so on). For bulk stored crops the situation is more akin to wheat, where direct physical traceability is not possible but identification of a pool of source crops is feasible.

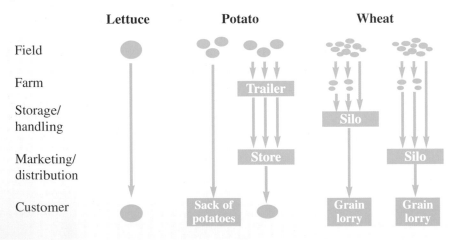

For products that are handled as discrete units, such as a single whole unit or box or bag of a product, these units may be identified to allow a defined source to be identified. Direct traceability to a single production source, including any treatments applied, is possible in this situation. However, for materials that are handled in bulk, such as barley and other cereals, it may not be possible for the product to be identified to allow a defined crop or source to be identified. In this instance, however, it is possible to allow for the identification of the different crops that make up the mixture. In this case direct traceability is not feasible but the identification of the source lots is. This is illustrated in Box 35.

Box 36 - The GM soya story: consequences for traceability and sourcing

Plants were first genetically modified (GM) in 1984 and GM crops became a commercial reality during the 1990s - first in the United States and then in Europe. The first commercial GM crop product in the UK was a canned tomato paste launched in February 1996. The tomatoes had been genetically modified to produce firmer fruits giving a thicker paste. Consumers were offered a choice as GM and conventional product were clearly labelled and sold alongside each other. The GM product sold well - a story which contrasts markedly with that of GM commodities such as soya and maize, as exemplified by the following summary of GM soya in the UK.

Soya is a source of many ingredients (e.g. soya flour, meal, protein, oil and the emulsifier lecithin) which are used in many food products (e.g. baked goods, dry soups, comminuted meat products, confectionery). Soya is a commodity crop with a long production and distribution chain: grown on a large scale, harvested beans are transported, mixed, warehoused, mixed with other batches, bought by brokers, sold on to ingredients suppliers, and processed to yield ingredients which themselves might be combined and redistributed.

The United States is at the forefront of biotechnology; products containing GM ingredients were widely accepted in the US by the mid-1990s. It is also a major producer of soyabeans. On commercial production in 1997, GM and non-GM soya entered the same chain (i.e. they were not segregated), so that any soya ingredient bought on the open market was potentially derived from a GM/non-GM mixture.

continued....

Approved for UK food use in 1995, GM soya reached the UK market from the US. This made it extremely difficult for food companies to give categorical assurances to customers and consumers as to whether their products did or did not contain GM soya. Some - for example the retailer Iceland - had already developed a 'GM-free' policy for their own products. In order to circumvent the problem, companies sought traceable and verifiable sources of non-GM soya.

This was a significant development for a crop with such a complex and international supply chain and in the UK it culminated in the development and publication of an industry-wide technical standard to help companies assure the supply of non-GM food ingredients and products. Although developed with GM soya and maize in mind, the system created was such that it could be applied to a whole range of supplies. This example dramatically illustrates the way in which supplier assurance and traceability have become integral parts of the food chain.

Further reading:

FDF/BRC (2001) Technical standard for the supply of identity preserved non-genetically modified food ingredients and product. Joint publication of the Food and Drink Federation and British Retail Consortium, published by The Stationery Office.

Jones, L. (1999) Genetically modified foods. British Medical Journal **318** 581-584

Jones, L. (1996) Food biotechnology: current developments and the need for awareness. Nutrition and Food Science **6** 5-11

Haine, H. (1999) The soyabean in brief. CCFRA Biotechnology Bulletin - Issue 10 pp10-13.

5.5 Food business supplier approval systems

If all sectors of the food chain take responsibility for food safety, legality and quality, food businesses using primary products will have appropriate systems in place for the control of these purchased goods as part of their own quality management and food safety systems. In general, these embody some form of supplier assurance procedures, which include controls on both the suppliers and the raw materials.

Controls on the raw materials generally involve agreeing specifications and, where appropriate, codes of conduct in respect of the production of the raw materials. This means that food businesses should ensure that appropriate specifications exist for raw materials and that these are agreed with relevant parties. The specification defines what is required to be supplied. A code of conduct will reference the relevant good practice protocols that will be followed in producing the primary product.

Similarly, food businesses should have procedures for approval and monitoring of suppliers. This often involves procedures for initial and on-going assessment of the standards of performance required. Assessments may take the form of monitoring performance or extend to supplier inspection. Typically the assessment may involve an examination of the production system and whether appropriate management and safety systems are in place. The mechanisms used can vary but may include only using suppliers that are registered with an appropriate assurance scheme.

5.6 The role of auditing

Having a quality assurance system in place does not necessarily guarantee that it will work. Auditing is used to evaluate the effectiveness of quality systems, to help ensure that the system is fulfilling its role. Audits also provide opportunities for challenging the system and developing it further, by identifying areas of weakness or ambiguity.

Audits can be classified on the basis of who is doing the audit and this might also help shape its purpose. Self-audits, conducted by someone within the business, are valuable both for checking that the system is working and familiarising staff with what to expect in an audit. Supplier auditing is conducted by food manufacturers and retailers, to check that their suppliers are operating to agreed procedures and standards. Third party auditing is often used where an 'independent' assessment is required - perhaps a retailer or manufacturer will use an independent organisation to audit a supplier on their behalf. This can often simplify the procedure so that a producer that supplies various companies can be audited once against a specified and commonly agreed system by a recognised third party rather than face separate audits from all their customers.

5.7 Conclusions

Quality assurance systems are now well established within the food industry and are becoming increasingly used at the primary production stage of the food supply chain. The emphasis with quality assurance is on 'prevention' - through appropriate management systems - in contrast to the retrospective approach embodied in quality control. Systems for ensuring that the primary producer meets the needs of their customer in producing raw materials which are safe and of the desired quality include HACCP, specifications and assurance schemes. Traceability can complement these by enabling the source of problems (or problem materials) to be identified. Auditing helps to ensure that the systems in place are being used properly.

These approaches are an important part of industry self-regulation, which is discussed on more detail in Chapter 6 on legislation and regulation.

6. AGRICULTURAL LEGISLATION AND REGULATION

Controls relating to food and agriculture are a mixture of statutory regulation and industry self-regulation. Generally, the former is the responsibility of the regulatory authorities that formulate legislation (e.g. European Commission, EU member state governments, the Federal and State authorities in the United States) and the relevant enforcement bodies (e.g. environmental health and trading standards officers in the UK). The task of ensuring that legislation is applied on a day-to-day basis is undertaken by the courts. In contrast, self-regulation is defined by non-governmental organisations including national and international bodies (e.g. trade organisations).

Agriculture is subject to detailed and extensive statutory regulatory controls which impinge on everything from general food safety and product liability through to specific aspects relating to crop and animal husbandry and product characteristics - for example pesticides, organic production, labelling and product quality. Self regulation on the other hand usually involves voluntary controls and adopted standards which help industry comply with legislation and customer demands and expectations as, for example, illustrated by various quality assurance initiatives.

The extent of statutory control and industry self regulation varies considerably from country to country and between economic regions. In many respects, industry self regulation in agriculture is more prevalent in the UK and EU than elsewhere in the world. However, this self regulation is having a wider 'knock-on' influence. For example, industries in countries exporting primary products to the UK and other EU member states are increasingly having to conform with standards or specifications which require adoption of procedures similar to UK/EU self-regulation as part of their commercial arrangement with their customer.

Because of this variation from region to region, it is not possible to describe legislation and self regulation in any great detail as it applies in various parts of the world. The purpose of this chapter is to demonstrate that agriculture is subject to regulatory controls, and to illustrate how legislation is used to control certain practices and how it works alongside voluntary controls. This section, therefore, provides outline examples of some UK controls (many of which originate from the EU), but it is not a definitive reference guide, and obviously the content of legislation and the way in which it is enforced will vary from country to country, and frequently changes.

6.1 Legislation - background

UK Acts and Statutory Instruments

Laws are made by the UK Parliament by drafting and passing of Acts of Parliament. These are complex procedures which usually take considerable time to develop and which, consequently, are difficult to revise. Since advances in knowledge will be made after an Act is passed, legislation is frequently reviewed to bring it up-to-date. In the UK this is achieved by the making of statutory instruments by the appropriate Ministers as authorised by Acts of Parliament. Statutory instruments can be amended or revoked by Ministers with the approval of Parliament and it is by this means that the 'parent' Act can remain in place for several years without revision.

For example, The Food Safety Act 1990 empowers Ministers to make regulations concerning the composition, safety, processing, hygiene, labelling and advertising of food, food sources and food contact materials; the control of novel foods and processes; the registration or licensing of food premises; and the hygiene training of food handlers. However, much of the detail of this is covered in statutory instruments passed since the introduction of the Act itself.

Implementation of EC Directives and Regulations

The Food Safety Act also empowers Ministers to make regulations for the implementation of EC Directives and for the enforcement of EC Regulations. Directives are required to be implemented by national legislation by a specific date.

Regulations are directly binding and apply to member states automatically; accordingly, there is no need for a national provision to implement them. However, details of who is responsible for enforcing the Regulation must be laid down and this is the responsibility of the member state.

Implementation of changes in legislation

UK Government Ministers have, in most instances, a legal obligation to circulate proposed regulations to interested parties, and in the light of comments received these can, if necessary, be amended prior to publication. Proposed changes to legislation might initially take the form of consultation documents which are widely circulated to interested parties.

Prior to the introduction of major pieces of legislation, proposals may be circulated in form of a 'green paper' or a 'white paper'. These describe in some detail the scope and extent of the proposals, the distinction between the two being that a green paper would usually contain a wider range of options and less emphasis on a preferred option or options.

Interpretation of the regulations

The interpretation of regulations in the context of legal proceedings is the responsibility of the courts. While advice on specific points may often be obtained from the Ministry making the regulations, it is always made clear that the Ministry has no power to interpret the legislation it drafts. When a prosecution is being considered, the proceedings may be influenced by previous court decisions - this is known as case law

Case law arises from past decisions of the higher courts and these decisions are often quoted by both the prosecution and the defence to lend support to their arguments. Such decisions may be used as guidance by local authorities in deciding whether or not to prosecute as well as by the courts when considering the evidence presented during hearings.

6.2 Legislation - some examples

The agriculture industry is subject to a significant level of legislation. This controls aspects of farming as diverse as inputs to the business (e.g. seeds, fertilisers, pesticides and veterinary medicines), worker safety, environmental protection, plant health and animal welfare. Harvested products are controlled by legislation on food safety, pesticides and contaminants. Particularly significant examples of UK legislation of direct relevance to the agricultural industry are outlined below.

UK Control of Pesticides Regulations 1986 (COPR)

These regulations provide a mechanism for the implementation of the aims of the Food and Environment Protection Act 1985 (FEPA). This requires that pesticides in the UK are approved by Ministers before they can be supplied, stored, advertised and used. Pesticide approval is for specific purposes (e.g. particular crops and diseases) and will stipulate the maximum number of applications, rate of use and interval between final application and harvest, which must be observed. The regulations also require that operators applying pesticides and those advising on their use are adequately trained.

UK Plant Protection Products Regulations 1995 (PPPR)

These regulations implement directive 91/414/EEC, the so called 'Authorisation Directive'. Thus it gives a framework for the harmonisation of approval systems for agricultural pesticides within the European Union and provides for an extensive 10 year review programme for all pesticides on the market before 1993. The directive also provides for the setting of MRLs for new active ingredients.

UK Pesticides (Maximum Residue Levels in Crops, Food and Feeding Stuffs) Regulations 1999

These regulations specify over 11,000 Maximum Residue Levels (MRLs). Further MRLs are planned, to implement a European programme to harmonise these across all member states. MRLs are defined as the maximum concentration of pesticide residue legally permitted in or on food commodities and animal feeds. These are based on Good Agricultural Practice (GAP) and are intended primarily as a check that GAP is being followed. Exposure to residues in excess of an MRL does not necessarily imply a risk to health (see Box 23 on p58).

Under these regulations it is an offence to put into circulation food products containing residues in excess of those prescribed. In order to comply with this legislation, food companies must ensure that pesticide residues in the raw materials supplied do not contravene the regulation. The regulations do, however, provide for a defence of due diligence. This means that a company found to be in breach of the regulations can offer as a defence evidence that it took all reasonable precautions to comply with the law.

UK Veterinary Residues - The Animals and Animal Products (Examination of Residues and Maximum Residue Limits) Regulations 1997

These regulations provide for controlled use in rearing of food animals, certain veterinary substances which have hormonal and antibiotic activity. They also lay down a community procedure for establishment of veterinary maximum residue levels for veterinary medicines. For example, they ban the processing of meat from an animal intended for human consumption which has been administered with any beta-agonist or hormonal substance. They also prohibit the sale for human consumption of any animal product which contains an unauthorised substance or an authorised substance exceeding its MRL. The concept of the 'withdrawal period' is also important. This is the time between the last dose given to the animal and the time at which the level of residues in the tissues (e.g. liver, muscle) or product (e.g. milk, eggs) is below or at the MRL.

UK Food Safety Act 1990

Anyone who sells food (or indeed offers food for sale) for human consumption is covered by this legislation. The definition of food includes such things as crops, fruits and vegetables as soon as they are harvested. Under the Act, food must be safe and of the nature, substance and quality demanded by the purchaser. This Act also permits a defence of due diligence; in mounting such a defence producers must show that they have taken all reasonable steps to avoid committing an offence.

Table 10 - Examples of other regulations that apply to UK agriculture

Welfare of Farmed Animals Regulations 2000

These Regulations implement a number of Community measures, and reflect the obligations contained in the European Convention for the Protection of Animals kept for Farming Purposes. The Regulations apply to all animals kept for farming purposes, subject to limited exemptions.

Groundwater Regulations 1998

These regulations implement the Groundwater Directive 80/86/EC controlling discharges of dangerous substances, including pesticides, sheep dip, heavy metals and ammonia. Persons disposing of such substances must have authorisation.

EC Regulation 2092/91 Organic Production of AgriProducts

This European Regulation describes the conditions which must be in place when crops or livestock are produced for marketing as organically grown products. Permitted inputs to organic systems are specified and management practices which are permitted in crop and livestock management are described.

Control of Substances Hazardous to Health Regulations 1999

These Regulations impose duties on employers to protect employees and others persons who may be exposed to substances hazardous to health. It also imposes certain duties on employees concerning their own protection from such exposure.

The Workplace (Health, Safety and Welfare) Regulations 1992

These Regulations give effect in part to Council Directive 89/654/EEC concerning the minimum safety and health requirements for the workplace. Amongst other provisions, the Regulations impose requirements with respect of maintenance, ventilation, indoor temperatures and thermometers, lighting, the suitability of work stations and the condition and arrangement of routes for pedestrians or vehicles.

UK Food Safety (General Food Hygiene) Regulations 1995

These regulations implement the EC directive on the hygiene of foodstuffs
(93/43EEC) in the UK. Food businesses must focus on activities in their operations
that are critical to food safety and find ways of controlling them. The Regulations
place an obligation on a proprietor of a food business to identify any step in the
activities of the food business which is critical to ensuring food safety and ensure
that adequate safety procedures are identified, implemented, maintained and
reviewed on the basis of the following principles:

◆   analysis of the potential food hazards in a food business operation;
◆   identification of the points in those operations where food hazards may occur;
◆   deciding which of the points identified are critical to ensuring food safety
    ("critical points");
◆   identification and implementation of effective control and monitoring
    procedures at those critical points; and
◆   review of the analysis of food hazards, the critical points and the control and
    monitoring procedures periodically, and whenever the food business's
    operations change.

Although not explicitly mentioned, this is often referred to as a 'HACCP
requirement' (see Chapter 5). However, it does not apply to primary production
(primary production in this context includes harvesting), nor does it apply to
products covered by other specific hygiene legislation (that is products of animal
origin). The various legislation that covers products of animal origin do also have a
HACCP requirement, which is more comprehensive as it requires documentation to
be kept for specified periods.

There is currently a complex set of legislation in the EU covering hygiene in
foodstuffs. The earliest of these date back over 35 years. Not all reflect a modern
risk based approach to food hygiene and in general this has meant a prescriptive
approach in many instances. There are in fact currently some 16 commodity
specific EC directives (such as those covering fresh meat, milk and fishery
products) in addition to the directive on general food hygiene which applies to all
other foodstuffs described here. As a result, the European Commission has
proposed a consolidation and simplification of all EU food hygiene legislation.

Box 37 - EU recast hygiene of foodstuffs legislation and farming

The European Commission has published a proposal for a regulation on the hygiene of foodstuffs, which is intended to replace the existing EU legislation. The proposed regulation states that food business operators *other than at the level of primary production* shall put in place, implement and maintain a permanent procedure developed in accordance with the principles of HACCP. The regulation will require food business operators to establish documents and records commensurate with the nature and size of the food business to demonstrate the effective application of HACCP.

Primary producers, however, while not subject to the full application of HACCP principles, will be required to monitor hazards to food safety and to eliminate or reduce these to an acceptable level. To achieve the required level of hygiene at farm level, it is suggested that possible hazards occurring in primary production and methods to control such hazards shall be addressed in guides to good practice.

The legislation also defines primary production as the production, rearing or growing of primary products up to and including harvesting, hunting, fishing and milking and all stages of animal production prior to slaughter. It is notable that other on-farm post-harvest activities, including activities such as storage, are not included in the definition of primary production - and might therefore be treated as a food business for which the requirements are more stringent.

There is no doubt that the legislation, if implemented as proposed, will have a significant effect at the farm level. The full implications however are not clear at present.

Further reading:

EC (2000) Draft European Commission proposals for the consolidation and simplification of EC food hygiene directives.
See www.foodstandards.gov.uk/consultations/eu_foodsafety.htm

The proposals are intended to achieve three broad aims.

◆   The first aim is the introduction of the 'farm to fork' principle to food safety covering all areas of food production including primary production.
◆   The second aim is for traceability of all food and food ingredients.
◆   The third aim is the transfer of the emphasis on the responsibility for production of safe food, away from enforcement authorities, to food producers.

All three aims have implications for the agri-food sector including primary producers. The third aim in particular will entail a move away from prescriptive legislation towards a more objective risk based approach. It is proposed that the measures shall apply from 1 January 2004.

Box 38 - Consumer Protection Act and farming

The Consumer Protection Act 1987 implements into UK law the provisions of the EC Directive (85/374/EEC) on Product Liability. The aim of this Act is to help safeguard the consumer from products that do not reach a reasonable level of safety. The Act imposes liability on producers for damage caused by defects in their products. An exception was given in the legislation to primary agricultural products (i.e. food sold in its raw state). However, Directive 1999/34/EEC amended the 1985 Product Liability Directive by removing this exemption. In the UK the scope of the Consumer Protection Act was extended in 2000 to primary agricultural products and game.

The amended Directive means strict liability now applies to all primary agricultural products (i.e. products of the soil, of stock-farming and fisheries) and game. Primary producers, therefore, are now subject to the same provisions of the Consumer Protection Act as all other parts of the food chain (such as processors and retailers). In this context producers include farmers and growers.

6.3 Self regulation and codes of practice

It would be impossible for legislation to adequately cover all the detailed aspects and practicalities of crop and animal husbandry. Although some specific aspects which require stringent regulation (e.g. pesticide controls) are covered in detail in a prescriptive manner, in most cases the controls are much more descriptive. This is often because what is applicable for different crop or stock production systems will depend on the nature of the product, the production process, and/or farming environment. By their nature, then, these legislative controls cannot be prescriptive in respect of the minutiae associated with agricultural production which therefore tend to be covered by codes of practice. It is a bit like the Highway Code in respect of using a car

In some instances, regulatory authorities will issue codes of practice to help compliance with legal obligations. In the UK, these would normally be drafted and issued by advisory committees of experts - such as the Advisory Committee on Pesticides. Codes of practice have the advantage that they are produced with the practicalities in mind and can be changed or updated without amending the legislation.

Pesticide legislation in the UK provides a good example. The legislation is very specific in terms of the uses of pesticides but the authorities felt that many of the practicalities relating to the safe use of pesticides, including worker and environmental safety, were appropriate to a code of practice. The guidance given in the code (*Code of practice for the safe use of pesticides - also known as the 'Green Code'*) is intended to help compliance with legal obligations by illustrating good practice and giving useful information. Following the code is not compulsory but if it is followed this will normally be enough to comply with the law. Also, following such a code can provide an important part of demonstrating due diligence should the need arise. In many respects codes of practice, standards and guidance notes written by and for industry serve the same purpose and are of equal importance in that they define good practice, that is, what is usual practice.

The guidelines used by industry are not just issued by regulatory authorities. They can be issued and authorised by numerous organisations, including professional bodies, research organisations, trade associations and other sector-specific trade bodies such as the levy boards. Furthermore, they may be national or international

**Table 11 - Examples of codes of practice covering
crop production**

- Code of Practice for the Safe Use of Pesticides on Farms and Holdings - The Green Code (MAFF, 1998).

- Code of Practice for Food Safety in the Fresh Produce Supply Chain in Ireland (Food Safety Authority of Ireland, 2001)

- The Control of Pesticides: a Code of Practice (Fresh Produce Consortium, 1997)

- The Air Code - Code of Good Agricultural Practice for the Protection of Air (MAFF, 1998)

- The Soil Code - Code of Good Agricultural Practice for the Protection of Soil (MAFF, 1998)

- The Water Code - Code of Good Agricultural Practice for the Protection of Water (MAFF, 1998)

- Code of Practice for the Management of Agricultural and Horticultural Waste (MAFF, 1998)

- Prevention of Environmental Pollution from Agricultural Activity (The Scottish Office, 1997)

- Code of Practice for Agricultural Use of Sewage Sludge (DETR, 1996)

- The Safe Sludge Matrix (ADAS, 2000)

- Code of Practice for the Control of *Salmonella* - during the storage, handling and transport of raw materials intended for incorporation into, or direct use as animal feedingstuffs (MAFF, 1995)

- Fertiliser Recommendations for Agricultural and Horticultural Crops (MAFF, 2000)

- The Grain Storage Guide (HGCA, 1999)

Table 12 - Examples of codes of practice relevant to livestock farming

- Clean livestock policy (Meat Hygiene Service, 1997)

- The 1998 strategy for the protection of animal welfare at livestock markets (MAFF, 1998)

- Guidance on the transport of casualty farm animals (MAFF, 1998)

- Welfare of red meat animals at slaughter - pre-slaughter handling: a pocket guide (MAFF, 1998)

- Code of practice for the prevention and control of *Salmonella* on pig farms (MAFF, 2000)

- Food safety and British pig meat - a briefing on food safety initiatives from farm to fork (Meat and Livestock Commission, 2000)

- Codes of recommendations for the welfare of livestock: pigs (MAFF, 1999)

- Clean beef cattle for slaughter. A guide for farmers (MAFF, 1999)

- Treatment and prevention of mastitis in dairy cows (MAFF, 1999)

- Beef production systems to enable cattle to be finished by 30 months of age (MAFF/ADAS, 1996)

- Code of practice for pasteurization of milk on farms and in small dairies (BSI, 1994)

- Pollution prevention guidelines: sheep dipping (Environment Agency, 1999)

- Clean sheep for slaughter - a guide for farmers (MAFF, 1999)

- Sheep dipping (Health and Safety Executive, 1997)

- Reducing water and effluent costs in poultry meat processing (DTI/DETR, 2000) 2000

- Code of practice prepared on behalf of the United Kingdom egg industry for those involved in the handling and storage of eggs from farm to retail sale (MAFF, 1996)

- Code of practice for the prevention and control of *Salmonella* in commercial egg laying flocks (MAFF, 1995)

- UKASTA code of practice for the manufacture of safe animal feedstuffs (UKASTA, 1997)

- Code of practice for the control of *Salmonella* during the storage, handling and transport of raw materials intended for incorporation into, or direct use as, animal feedingstuffs (MAFF, 1995)

- Code of practice for distributors registered for the sale, supply and storage of licensed animal medicines and medicated animal feedingstuffs (MAFF, 1991) in their scope. The technical content is usually provided by technical experts and practitioners from within industry and/or government. A selection of these, mostly drawn from the UK, are listed in Tables 11 and 12 to give a flavour of the topics covered.

In general the guidance given in these guidelines will help industry comply with legislation and, where appropriate, meet additional customer demands and/or expectations. In some respects they may be described as 'how-best-to-do' instructions. They help industry by:

♦   illustrating good practice;
♦   giving practical advice; and
♦   giving other useful information.

A good example of a code of practice with international status is provided by the Codex Alimentarius Commission guidance on the general principles of food hygiene throughout the food chain (Box 39 - p112). The document follows the food chain from primary production through to final consumption, highlighting the key hygiene controls at each stage. The controls described are internationally recognised as essential to ensure safety and suitability of food for consumption. The General Principles are commended to governments, the food industry (including primary producers) and consumers alike.

Box 39 - Codex Alimentarius Food Hygiene Basic Texts

In keeping with its mission to protect the health of consumers, the Codex Alimentarius Commission published three basic texts on food hygiene. As well as appearing in the Codex Alimentarius itself, these internationally recognised texts have been published in a small stand-alone volume to encourage their adoption by everyone across the food chain. The three texts are:

♦ An international code of practice on the general principles of food hygiene
♦ HACCP and its application
♦ Microbiological criteria for foods

The general principles text impinges directly on primary production. It states that primary production should be managed in a way that ensures that food is safe and suitable for its intended use, and that where necessary, this should include:

♦ avoiding the use of areas where the environment poses a threat to the safety of food;
♦ controlling contaminants, pests and disease of animals and plants in such a way as not to pose a threat to food safety; and
♦ adopting practices and measures to ensure that food is produced under appropriate hygienic conditions.

It goes on to explain that the rationale for this is to reduce the likelihood of introducing a hazard which may adversely affect the safety of food, or its suitability for consumption, at later stages of the food chain. It then states a series of principles with regard to environmental hygiene, hygienic production practices, handling, storage, and transport, and cleaning and maintenance.

Further reading:

Codex Alimentarius Commission (2001) Food Hygiene Basic Texts. Second edition. FAO/WHO. ISBN 92 5 104619 0

7. Conclusions

The relationship between the agricultural and food sectors has changed significantly in recent years - and continues to do so. Historically, farmers produced food raw materials and fresh produce, most of which was either sold-on through a marketing organisation and/or the produce had a virtual guaranteed market through some form of official support mechanism. For the primary producer, the end use of the material was of relatively little concern. Similarly, the food industry bought their raw materials with little thought of where or how it was produced - they bought off an intermediary and had little direct contact with primary production. For both the agricultural and food sectors, these historical patterns of trading with each other are now long gone.

In today's market place the position is reversed - farmers now have to be much more aware of market demand and of the needs of their customers in terms of the safety, legality and quality of their produce. They now produce product in a much more defined and controlled manner to statutory and self-regulatory requirements - to assure its suitability for the intended use and its safety to the consumer. Likewise food businesses are having to consider their raw materials not just in terms of food safety and quality, but in terms of how it is produced and how this affects the 'extended' product (e.g. welfare and environmental messages on the label).

Today the food production chain is highly integrated. Companies at each stage and, to some extent, within different sectors are much more dependent on each other. They are also much more 'in tune' with the needs and wants of consumers - they gather and use marketplace information not only to shape and develop new products, but to adjust existing products and processes in ways which help to maintain and/or extend their market share. Through better communication and closer relationships along the food production chain - and through systems such as quality and safety assurance, product specifications, auditing, traceability, and consumer feedback - the food production process is becoming less the work of a series of independent businesses and more a concerted whole. In short, farmers are now having to look past the farm gate, while the food businesses they supply are having to look back over that gate.

8. GLOSSARY

This short glossary provides a guide to some common agri-related terms and acronyms that can sometimes cause confusion. It is intended to provide simple and meaningful explanations, reflecting the general use of the terms, rather than providing precise technical or legal definitions. Where the term is covered in greater detail within the text, a pointer to the relevant page, box or section is given.

Active ingredient - Sometimes called active agent (especially in the US), this is the component of a pesticide that is biologically active. For example, in a fungicide preparation, the active ingredient is the chemical which kills the target fungus.

Agriculture - this is an all embracing term to describe the cultivation of plants and raising of animals for food and other materials. Horticulture is usually viewed as a part of agriculture and relates particularly to the cultivation of vegetables, fruits, flowers, and ornamental shrubs and trees. Agronomy refers to the theory and practice of crop production and land/soil management.

Arable - in its true sense, the term arable is used to describe land which is used for growing crops. However, it also used more specifically to describe farming of 'broad acre' crops such as cereals and oilseed as distinct from horticulture which includes cultivation of fruits and vegetables. This use of arable is more arbitrary, however, as some regard some crops (e.g. potatoes) as falling within arable farming while others regard them as falling within horticulture.

Aquaculture - the farming of water animals (e.g. fish, crustaceans) and plants (e.g. seaweed). Mariculture refers specifically to the cultivation of marine species in salt water.

Biological control - a system of controlling agricultural pests and pathogens by using natural predators or diseases of the pests or pathogens themselves to prevent them from establishing.

Biosolids - the organic by-product of urban waste-water treatment. It is also known as sewage sludge and is relatively rich in plant nutrients and can, therefore, be used as a manure. The 'safe sludge matrix' (see p48) was developed to assure safe use of biosolids.

Bolting - botanically, this is the development of flower stems (leading to the formation of flowers and eventually seeds) in plants which grow in a 'rosette' habit, such as beet, lettuce and brassicas. These biennial plants normally grow as a rosette (i.e. compressed stem/head) in the first year and flower the following year in response to a cold spell during winter and the lengthening days of spring. Some varieties of these crops are more susceptible to bolting than others. For the more susceptible varieties, a short cold spell in autumn followed by a spell of warmer weather while the days are relatively long, can be enough to trigger bolting which, from an agricultural viewpoint, is obviously undesirable.

British Farm Standard - this is an assurance that products carrying the 'Little Red Tractor' logo are produced to specified food hygiene, environmental and animal welfare standards which are monitored through recognised assurance schemes. Products covered include meat, poultry, milk, cereals, vegetables, fruit and salads. For further information see page 87.

CAP - the Common Agricultural Policy (of the European Union). See entry under GATT and Section 1.4 (p9).

Codex Alimentarius - the word 'Codex' is used as shorthand in two ways. On the one hand it is used to refer to the Codex Alimentarius Commission. This is an organisation which is part of the United Nations FAO/WHO (Food and Agricultural Organisation / World Health Organisation) Commission on Food Standards. Its role is to simplify and integrate food quality and safety standards for recognition internationally. These are published as the Codex Alimentarius (the 'food code'). The codes of practice, guidelines and recommendations that make up the code help to facilitate international trade. For example, Codex MRLs may be used as a presumptive standard where no MRL for a particular pesticide/commodity exists in law. For further information see page 13.

Compost - Composting is a biological process in which micro-organisms break down organic materials, particularly plant tissues. As a result of the composting process the physical nature of the material is changed to a humus-rich substrate and plant nutrients are made more readily available. Heat is also generated and as a result unwanted micro-organisms including pathogens may be eliminated. Compost is the decayed product of the composting process.

Cultivar and variety - a variety is a sub-division within a species. From an agricultural viewpoint, a variety can be regarded as a group of similar plants that can be distinguished from other groups within the same species. A cultivar ('cultivated variety') is a plant variety that has been cultivated, and is maintained by cultivation, rather than having arisen naturally.

Early / late varieties - a term used to identify a crop variety which reaches maturity (e.g. vegetable, fruit or flower formation) earlier or later than the main crop.

Extended product - the idea that in addition to a product's sensory, chemical and biological characteristics, some consumers also perceive its quality as including wider issues such as production methods, animal welfare, and environmental impact.

Fallow - land which is left unplanted in order to restore its fertility

Farmyard manure (FYM) - the excrement of farm animals (faeces and urine) often mixed with straw or other organic materials, particularly from animal bedding. It may contain pathogens. FYM should be left for a period of time and/or composted to reduce these pathogens. It should be at least partially rotted before application to soil.

Fertiliser - material added to the soil to improve its fertility, that is, to increase the levels of plant nutrients. Fertilisers may be natural (e.g. manures) or artificial (defined mixtures of the major inorganic nutrients required by plants).

Fodder, forage, hay, straw and silage - These are related terms with slightly different meanings. The term fodder is usually used to describe dried plant material, such as hay, used for livestock feed. Hay is leafy material (usually dried mown grass) whereas straw is stalk (stem) material with a coarser texture. Silage, by comparison, is moist crop material (e.g. grass, clover) that has been preserved by fermentation in a closed container (clamp). The term forage also refers to plant leaf and stalk material for animal feed and which is either grazed green, grazed dried or fed preserved.

Food safety hazard - A food safety hazard is a biological (e.g. micro-organism such as a bacterial pathogen), chemical (e.g. pesticide residue) or physical (e.g. foreign body such as glass) agent which has an adverse effect on consumer health. In contrast, a food quality issue is a biological (e.g. spoilage organism such as bacterial and fungal rot and moulds), chemical (e.g. compositional attribute such as dry matter and sugar content) or physical (e.g. foreign body such as a pest and product defect such as other vegetable matter) agent which adversely affects the acceptability of the product to the customer and/or consumer, without affecting safety.

Fungicide - see pesticide

GAP - Good Agricultural Practice is a term which is widely used but rarely formally defined. In relation to food production, GAP can be considered as the use of practices and systems which comply with the law and which result in the production of safe and wholesome food. With regards to pesticides, for example, GAP requires that the pesticide is used strictly in accordance with the instructions provided, controlling the pest but leaving the minimum possible residue which is also below the relevant MRL. GAP is now also being considered from an environmental perspective, so that the adoption of GAP will minimise possible adverse environmental effects of agriculture, as achievable through the LEAF system, for example (Linking Environment and Farming - see p40-41).

GATT - this stands for General Agreement on Tariffs and Trade. GATT was implemented in 1948 to help liberalise multilateral trading as part of the post-war reconstruction process. In simple terms GATT specifies ground rules - relating to factors such as agricultural subsidies, barriers to import, and export subsidies - to help facilitate international trade. This has had implications for the EU's Common Agricultural Policy (CAP). The World Trade Organisation (WTO) was established in 1995 following the conclusion of the last round (Uruguay Round) of GATT negotiations, in order to take future negotiations forward. For further information see Section 1.4 (p9).

Genetically modified organisms (GMO) - these are generally regarded as organisms in which the genetic material (DNA) has been altered in a way that does not occur naturally by mating and/or natural recombination. This definition forms the basis of the legal definition of GMOs in EU legislation (EU 90/220) controlling the use of GMOs. It includes instances where DNA has been extracted from organisms and re-introduced into them by laboratory procedures but specifically excludes procedures such as in vitro fertilisation, cell fusion, and established techniques, such as mutagenesis, used in conventional breeding. For further information see pages 4 and 95.

HACCP - pronounced 'Hass-up', this acronym stands for Hazard Analysis Critical Control Point. It is well established within food processing and manufacturing, and is increasingly being adopted in agricultural food production, to assure the safety of food products. It is based on scrutinising a production process to identify specific hazards and where they might arise, and then targeting appropriate control measures at the steps in the process (the critical control points) at which the hazard is best controlled. An important part of HACCP is the monitoring of controls to check that they are working, and the on-going review of the HACCP system to take account of changes to the process or new hazards. For further information see pages 88-91.

Harvest interval - this is the period which must elapse between the last application of a pesticide and the harvesting of a crop for human or animal consumption. The harvest interval is a condition of approval of the pesticide and is quoted on the pesticide container label. Adhering to harvest intervals is an important part of good agricultural practice (GAP) and not adhering to them is an offence. For further information see pages 58-59.

Herbicide - see pesticide

Horticulture - see agriculture

Husbandry - traditionally this term refers to the skills and systems used to raise crops and/or livestock but is sometimes used synonymously with farming or to specify particular aspects of farming (e.g. animal husbandry).

Hybrid and hybrid vigour - a hybrid is the offspring resulting from a cross between two parents that are genetically different. In extreme cases, the parents may be from different species or even from different genera (a genus is a group of closely related species). The production of hybrids has found practical use, because of the phenomenon of hybrid vigour. This is the increase in size and vigour of a hybrid over the best parent. In crops, for example, it may be apparent through plant height, leaf size, root size, seed size or number, disease resistance and so on. The term F1-hybrid is often encountered - F1 is a term from genetics and means the first generation following a cross (it is short for first filial generation).

Hydroponics - a system for growing plants without soil. In its strict sense, the roots are allowed to grow in a nutrient solution but, more loosely, the term is sometimes applied where the roots are allowed to develop in an artificial substrate which is nutritionally inert. In either case, the composition of the nutrient solution can be closely controlled, allowing optimisation of nutrient delivery to the crop.

Insecticide - see pesticide.

Integrated farm management (IFM) - an approach to farming which combines the best traditional approaches with appropriate modern technology to balance the need for economic production with positive environmental management. Integrated crop management (ICM) is a related term used to describe integrated systems applied to crops. The term integrated pest management (IPM) is also used with regard to pest control. This involves an integrated balance of biological, chemical, cultural and mechanical control methods. For further information see pages 40-41.

Levy boards - these are UK organisations which are charged with maintaining expertise and/or specific technical and other services in support of particular sectors of the industry and which are funded by a levy (some voluntary and some statutory) upon the sector they serve. Examples include the Meat and Livestock Commission (MLC), the Home Grown Cereals Authority (HGCA), the Processors and Growers Research Organisation (beans, peas and pulses), the Horticultural Development Council (HDC), and the British Potato Council.

Lodging - this is a form of damage to field crops such as cereals where they bend, break or lie flat in the field. Lodging can be caused by adverse weather (wind and rain), nutritional factors (e.g. high soil nitrogen), some diseases or pests (e.g. the corn borer in maize), and high planting density.

Low input systems - the term 'inputs' refers to the materials required to farm a crop or animal, and includes materials such as seed, fertiliser, pesticide, animal feed, veterinary medicines and even fuel for machinery. The term 'low input systems' is sometimes used by way of contrast with the term 'intensive' farming in which greater amounts of materials and energy are used to maximise productivity.

Manure - a generic term for waste organic substances used as a fertiliser and/or soil conditioner and includes animal manure, faecal material (human or animal) and composted organic materials. Farmyard manure, animal slurry and biosolids, for example, are all generally classed as manures when applied to agricultural land.

Maximum Residue Level (MRL) - an MRL is the maximum concentration of a pesticide that is legally permitted in or on a foodstuff after the use of the pesticide in accordance with good agricultural practice (GAP). MRLs are primarily intended to provide a check that good agricultural practice is being followed (e.g. to help international trade), and apply to agricultural commodities not processed foods. MRLs are not safety limits - so that eating a food containing a pesticide above its MRL does not automatically imply a health risk. In the UK, some MRLs originate from national (UK) legislation, some from EU legislation and some from Codex Alimentarius. For further information see pages 58-59.

National and Recommended Lists of varieties - these are lists of varieties of crops assessed and deemed suitable for cultivation on a commercial scale in the UK. Before a new variety of crop can be marketed within the UK it has to get on to the National List (so called NL varieties). This it does through a series of statutory trials through which it has to be demonstrated that the new variety offers a clear improvement in agronomic value for cultivation and use (VCU) relative to other varieties on the National List. As National Lists can be quite long (e.g. 30-60 varieties for wheat and barley), varieties that are shown to offer significant advantages in further voluntary trials can move on to the Recommended List (so called Recommended List varieties). The aim of the system is to encourage the continuous improvement in available varieties, and the efficient and orderly movement of these varieties through development to market. Varieties appearing on the RL gain significant commercial advantage; seed certification statistics suggest that over 90% of seed certified in the UK is of RL varieties.

Organic farming - in general terms this is a system of farming which advocates the use of 'natural' rather than 'artificial' forms of pest and disease control and fertilisers. In practice the concept is more difficult than first seems as the distinction between natural and artificial can be somewhat arbitrary. In the EU there are specific criteria that have to be fulfilled before the claim can be made that an operation or product is organic and, in the UK, organic operations must register with and be inspected by a UKROFS approved body. UKROFS is the UK Register of Organic Food Standards. It was established in 1987 to provide baseline organic standards and to approve and monitor the work of organic certification bodies, such as the Organic Food Federation and the Soil Association. For further information see pages 20 (Box 8), 34 (Box 12) and 36 (Box 13).

Parasite - a term describing an organism that lives in or upon another organism (termed the host) and at its expense (e.g. by taking food from it without returning any benefit). Liver fluke (*Fasciola hepatica*), a flatworm which infects and can kill cattle and sheep, is an example of an animal parasite, while plant pathogens (see below) such as moulds are also parasitic. The comparison is often drawn between parasitism and symbiosis. In the latter, both participants benefit from the relationship. For example, nitrogen fixing bacteria live in nodules on the roots of leguminous crops (peas and beans), obtaining food and shelter from the plant in exchange for nitrogen in a form that the plant can utilise.

Pathogen - an organism that causes disease. For example, plant pathogens that can affect crops include certain fungi (moulds), bacteria and viruses. Pathogens usually infect a specific plant or animal, or group of plants or animals and, if untreated, can cause substantial losses. Some pathogens are spread by pests - for example, aphids transmit certain plant viruses. Human pathogens, including bacteria, protozoa and viruses, cause human disease. As some pathogens - mostly bacteria such as *Salmonella*, *Listeria* and *E.coli* O157:H7 - are foodborne, they are of concern to the food industry which has to adopt stringent measures to help control them. For further information see page 64.

Pest - an organism which damages crops, livestock or stored product, either directly or indirectly (e.g. by infecting it with a disease). If uncontrolled, pests can cause significant losses. Examples of pests include aphids which can transmit diseases in crops, insects which infest and damage grain during storage, and ticks which spread disease amongst livestock.

Pesticide - a chemical used to control diseases, insects and weeds that can harm or destroy crops or the food products derived from them. Some pesticides are man-made (synthetic) and some occur naturally. Different pesticides fulfil different roles. For example, insecticides kill and control insects, fungicides are used to control fungi (moulds) and herbicides (weed killers) are used to control weeds. For further information see Section 2.2.

Plant breeders rights (PBR) - in many countries plant breeders can protect new plant varieties that they develop under a system of plant breeders rights. This enables breeders to control the multiplication of protected seed and collect royalties on the sale of the seed. Although protection is implemented through national law, so the system varies from one country to another, most countries that operate a system will have joined UPOV (International Union for the Protection of New Varieties of Plants) and use the UPOV Convention as the basis for their legislation. New varieties have to fulfil the so-called DUS-test before they can be recognised as new - that is be sufficiently distinct (D - distinctness) from other varieties, produce populations that are uniform (U - uniformity) and be genetically stable (S - stability) so that their characteristics are stably inherited through subsequent generations. PBR is also sometimes referred to as PVP (Plant Variety Protection).

Pre-emergence / post-emergence - this refers to the applications of pesticides before or after emergence of the crop (i.e. the appearance of seedlings). For example, a herbicide to which the seedlings would be sensitive might be applied before they appear (pre-emergence) to minimise competition from weeds.

Primary production - this means the production, rearing or growing of primary products up to and including harvesting, milking and all stages of animal production prior to slaughter. Primary product means products of the soil (i.e. crops) and of stock farming.

Quality assurance (QA) and quality control (QC) - Quality assurance is the philosophy of setting up and implementing management controls to assure that the end product is of the desired quality. In contrast, quality control involves the testing of the end product to ensure that it meets stipulated requirements. Quality assurance can therefore be regarded as 'preventative' while quality control is essentially 'retrospective'. However, quality control can form part of quality assurance - for example where a raw material or prepared ingredient is subject to QC testing before use in the manufacture of a multi-component food. The food industry has seen a large shift away from end-product testing in favour of preventative assurance systems in recent years. For further information see Chapter 5.

Quality management (or Total Quality Management - TQM) - this is a formalised approach to trying to get things right - that is, to manage the quality of a product or service and so consistently achieve an appropriate standard. A good quality management system is based on two main components: a commitment to the philosophy of getting things right and a system of practical procedures to help ensure this. It is important to note that TQM applies not just to the technical operations but to all aspects of a business. For further information see Chapter 5.

Rotation - growing one or more crops in succession on the same piece of land in successive years. During the agricultural revolution in 18th century Britain, productivity increased enormously as a result of Lord Townsend's four-field system in which fields - which under the three-field system would have been left fallow - were planted with clover or turnips and then used to feed animals and/or ploughed-in to restore fertility.

Set-aside - the system under which a proportion of the land used to produce a particular commodity is left idle in order to reduce the supply of the commodity (e.g. one in surplus) and the associated costs of its production.

Slurry - a generic term used to describe a liquid mixture of farm animal urine and faeces. It may contain pathogens, most notably *E.coli* O157 and *Salmonella* species. Treatment to reduce these pathogens is usually of the passive type, that is through the passage of time.

SOLA - Specific Off-Label Approval. Pesticides have to be approved and their use has to comply with statutory conditions accompanying the approval. These conditions are stated on the product label and include the crop(s) and pest(s) for which the pesticide was developed. Often the pesticide will be of use for protecting crops other than those for which it was initially improved - such as diseases of relatively minor crops - in which case additional 'Off-label' approval can be granted.

Spring variety - see entry under winter variety.

Tillage - preparation of land for growing crops, including ploughing and weed removal. Minimum tillage systems - in which the top layer of soil is moved but not inverted, as it is with ploughing - attempt to minimise disturbance of the soil to limit factors such as erosion, soil loss and nutrient leaching and reduce the energy and labour costs compared with ploughing.

Traceability - the facility to trace the source of food products or their ingredients. Traceability is much simpler for 'identity preserved' single products (e.g. a lettuce) with a short supplier-distributor chain than for ingredients used in multi-component products (e.g. vegetable oil in a ready-meal). There is growing emphasis on traceability within the food chain in relation to quality management, safety and quality assurance, product recall, and liability issues, for example. For further information see Section 5.4 (p91) including Boxes 34, 35 and 36.

Weed and volunteer - a weed is a plant growing where it is not wanted. If weeds are allowed to establish and thrive in a crop then they can provide significant competition for light, nutrients and water and so adversely affect productivity. Weeds present in crops at harvest time can pose a hazard in the harvested crop - for example, the weed might produce poisonous seeds (e.g. nightshade) or become a foreign body in the product (e.g. hard seeds). A 'volunteer' is a weed which results from a crop. If, at the end of its season, the crop releases seeds which germinate and become weeds to other crops on the same ground in subsequent growing season, the weeds are referred to as 'volunteers'. One example is oilseed rape which can produces volunteer weeds in following crops. Another example is sugar beet - if some of the plants bolt (see above) and produce seeds, these can become weeds in subsequent crops.

Winter variety - varieties of crops such as winter wheat and winter rape which are sown in the autumn and spend the winter as young plants and then mature in the late spring / early summer of the following year. In contrast, spring varieties (e.g. spring wheat) are sown in spring and harvested in the summer of the same year.

World Trade Organisation - see entry under GATT and Section 1.4 (p9).

Yield - the amount of product resulting from cultivation of a crop or keeping of livestock.

9. FURTHER READING

The items listed here provide additional useful information and background reading. Trade journals are commercially produced magazine-type publications targeted at specific sectors of industry. Material published in trade journals is not usually peer reviewed and tends to be a mix of factual information and opinion. As they are a very good way of learning about the current issues, concerns and developments in a sector, examples of UK agriculture trade journals are listed.

This section also lists some websites that contain useful information on food agriculture and agricultural practices. Note, however, that whilst websites are convenient and useful sources of information, they vary considerably in the level and reliability of the coverage they provide. Most of the material found on the web is not subject to peer review and validation. Website addresses quoted here were live at the time the book was written but are prone to change; however, live links can often be found from the websites of RASE (www.rase.org.uk) and CCFRA (www.campden.co.uk) or by using a common search engine.

Books, guides and articles

Anon. (1990) Exploited plants: collected papers from Biologist. Institute of Biology, London.

Bedford, L. and Knight, C. (2001) HACCP in agriculture: livestock production. CCFRA Guideline No. 33. A series of livestock-specific HACCP case studies which complement this generic guide are also available.

Bender, D.A. and Bender, A.E. (2000) Benders' dictionary of nutrition and food technology (seventh edition). Woodhead Publishing Ltd.

Brown, K.L. and Oscroft, C.A. (1989) Guidelines for the hygienic manufacture, distribution and retail sale of sprouted seeds with particular reference to mung beans. CCFRA Technical Manual No. 25.

Codex Alimentarius Commission (2001) Understanding the Codex Alimentarius. Codex Alimentarius Commission on the website of the Food and Agriculture Organisation: www.fao.org

Curry, D. (2002) Farming and food: a sustainable future. Report of the Policy Commission on the Future of Farming and Food. Available from the cabinet office website at: http://www.cabinet-office.gov.uk/farming

Cybulska, G. (2000) Waste management in the food industry: an overview. Key Topic in Food Science and Technology No. 2. CCFRA

DEFRA (2001) World Trade Organisation Agreement on Agriculture. UK Department for Environment, Food and Rural Affairs website: www.defra.gov.uk/farm/wto/wtopaper.htm

DEFRA/HGCA (2002) Arable cropping and the environment - a guide.

DTI (2001) World trade and international trade rules. UK Department of Trade and Industry website: www.dti.gov.uk/worldtrade/subject.htm

Duddington, C.L. (1969) Useful plants. McGraw Hill.

Emsley, J. (1994) The consumer's good chemical guide - a jargon free guide to the chemicals of everyday life. W.H. Freeman.

European Union (1989) A common agricultural policy of the 1990s (5th Edition). Office for Official Publications of the European Communities

FSA (2001) Survey of milk for mycotoxins. FSA Food Survey Information Sheet No. 17/01. Food Standards Agency, London, UK.

Haine, H. (1999) The soyabean in brief. CCFRA Biotechnology Bulletin - Issue 10 pp10-13.

Herren, R.V and Donahue, R.L. (1991) The agriculture dictionary. Delmar Publishers Inc.

Heywood, U.H. and Chant, S.R. (1982) Popular encyclopedia of plants. Cambridge University Press.

Hutton, T. (2001) Food manufacturing: an overview. Key Topics in Food Science and Technology No. 3. CCFRA.

Jones, L. (1999) Genetically modified foods. British Medical Journal **318** 581-584

Jones, L. (1996) Food biotechnology: current developments and the need for awareness. Nutrition and Food Science **6** 5-11

Jones, L. (2001) Molecular methods in food analysis: principles and examples. Key Topics in Food Science and Technology No. 1. CCFRA.

Knight, C. and Stanley, R. (2000) HACCP in agriculture and horticulture (second edition). CCFRA Guideline No. 10. A series of crop-specific HACCP case studies which complement this generic guide are also available.

Leake, A. (2001) Integration: farm and environment. Biologist **48** 159-162.

MAFF (1989) Code of practice for the control of salmonellae in the production of final feed for livestock in premises producing over 10,000 tonnes per annum. *MAFF Leaflet PB 0018.*

Marsh, J. (2001) Agriculture in the UK - its role and challenge. UK Department of Trade and Industry. www.foresight.gov.uk

Moore, D.M. (Ed) (1982) Green planet: the story of plant life on earth. pp238-248. Domestication of plants. Cambridge University Press.

POST (1997) Safer eating - microbiological food poisoning and its prevention. Parliamentary Office of Science and Technology, ISBN 1 897941 56 0.

Smartt, J. and Simmonds, N.W. (1995) Evolution of crop plants. Second edition. Longman Scientific and Technical.

Smith, J.E. (2001) Mycotoxins pp238-259 in Food Chemical Safety - Volume 1: Contaminants. Watson, D. (Ed) Woodhead Publishing. ISBN 1 85573 462 1.

Soffe, R.J. (1995) The agricultural notebook. 19th edition. Blackwell Science.

Stadig, M. (2001) Life cycle assessment of apple production: case studies for Sweden, New Zealand and France. SIK Report No. 683 - Swedish Institute for Food and Biotechnology

Timperley, A.W. (2000) Heat processed poultry feed: hygienic design of post-process production and transportation equipment. CCFRA Guideline No. 30.

Tinker, P.B. (Ed) (2000) Shades of green - a review of UK farming systems. Royal Agricultural Society of England. ISBN: 0 902629 99 9

Vaughan, J.G and Geissler, C.A. (1997) The new Oxford book of food plants. Oxford University Press.

WTO (2001) Trading into the future. World Trade Organization website: www.wto.org/

Zervoudaki, S. (2000) The CAP reform - a policy for the future. Factsheet of European Commission - Directorate General of Agriculture.

Trade Journals

Arable Farming, Miller Freeman UK Ltd., 4 Friars Courtyard, Princes Street, Ipswich, IP1 1RJ

Grain & Feed Milling Technology, Turret RAI plc, Armstrong House, 38 Market Square, Uxbridge, Middlesex UB8 1TG

Crops, Reed Business Information, Quadrant House, The Quadrant, Sutton, Surrey, SM2 5AS

Farmers Weekly, Reed Business Information, Quadrant House, The Quadrant, Sutton, SM2 5AS

Fresh Produce Journal, Lockwood Press Ltd., 430-438 Market Towers, 1 Nine Elms Lane, Vauxhall, London SW8 5NN

Grower, Nexus House, Swanley, Kent. BR8 8HU

Independent Farm Business News, Montague House, Dunstanville Terrace, Falmouth, Cornwall TR11 2SW

Milk Industry International, 59 Coleridge Close, Hitchen, Hertfordshire, SG4 0QX

Pesticides Outlook, The Royal Society of Chemistry, Thomas Graham House, Science Park, Milton Road, Cambridge CB4 0WF

Websites

British Farm Standard - www.littleredtractor.org.uk

Campden & Chorleywood Food Research Association (CCFRA) - www.campden.co.uk

Codex Alimentarius Commission - www.codexalimentarius.net

Crop Protection Association - www.cropprotection.org.uk

FAO (Food and Agriculture Organisation of the United Nations) - www.fao.org

LEAF (Linking Environment and Farming) - www.leafuk.org

National Farmers Union - www.nfu.org.uk

NIAB (National Institute of Agricultural Botany - UK) - www.niab.com

Royal Agricultural Society of England (RASE) - www.rase.org.uk

UK Department for the Environment, Food and Rural Affairs (DEFRA) - www.defra.gov.uk

UK Food Standards Agency - www.food.gov.uk

UK Home Grown Cereals Authority (HGCA) - www.hgca.co.uk

UK Horticultural Development Council - www.hdc.org.uk

UK Meat and Livestock Commission - www.mlc.org.uk

UK Pesticides Safety Directorate (PSD) - www.pesticides.gov.uk

USDA (United States Department of Agriculture) - www.usda.gov